ACCELERATING THAILAND'S E-MOBILITY TRANSITION

POLICY ASSESSMENT AND ACTION PLAN 2025–2035

DECEMBER 2025

ACGF
ASEAN CATALYTIC GREEN FINANCE FACILITY
An ASEAN Infrastructure Fund Initiative

ADB

6 ADB Avenue, Mandaluyong City, 1550 Metro Manila, Philippines
Tel +63 2 8632 4444; Fax +63 2 8636 2444
www.adb.org

ISBN 978-92-9277-629-9 (print); 978-92-9277-630-5 (PDF); 978-92-9277-631-2 (ebook)
Publication Stock No. TCS250562-2
DOI: http://dx.doi.org/10.22617/TCS250562-2

Notes:
In this publication, "CNY" refers to the Chinese yuan, "€" refers to euros, "INR" refers to Indian rupees, "W" refers to Korean won, "B" refers to Thai baht, and "$" refers to United States dollars, unless otherwise stated.

ADB recognizes "China" as the People's Republic of China, "Korea" and "South Korea" as the Republic of Korea, and "Vietnam" as Viet Nam.

Cover design by Rocilyn Locsin Laccay. Winding road photo from stock.adobe.com. Charging station photo by ADB.

Printed on recycled paper

CONTENTS

TABLES AND FIGURES

TABLES

FIGURES

FOREWORD

Thailand's recent commitment to achieve net-zero emissions by 2050 places the transport sector at the center of its climate transition. Electrifying freight and passenger transport, supported by a stronger domestic electric vehicle manufacturing industry and an expanded charging network, is central to this effort.

This *Accelerating Thailand's E-Mobility Transition: Policy Assessment and Action Plan 2025–2035* provides a road map to accelerate Thailand's transition to cleaner transport. It assesses the current e-mobility landscape, identifies policy and infrastructure gaps, and offers practical recommendations for reform and investment. The report focuses on advancing sustainable urban and intercity mobility through policy development and investment planning, highlighting opportunities to scale electric bus, or e-bus, deployment and supporting infrastructure nationwide. Anchored on the proposed Thailand E-Mobility Mission 2025–2035, the plan outlines 50 measures across demand, supply, and infrastructure to guide coordinated action and scale up investment.

Commissioned by and developed in partnership with the Ministry of Transport and the Office of Transport and Traffic Policy and Planning, the plan connects policy with investment to mobilize private capital, strengthen coordination, and create new opportunities for Thai businesses and workers in the growing regional e-mobility market.

The report also reflects the Asian Development Bank's partnership approach through the ASEAN Catalytic Green Finance Facility (ACGF). By combining technical assistance, policy reform, and concessional finance, ACGF supports governments in translating climate commitments into investment-ready projects. Thailand's leadership in e-mobility demonstrates how innovation and collaboration can translate policy goals into tangible results that drive inclusive and sustainable growth.

As Thailand and its partners move into this decisive decade, this action plan serves as both a road map and an invitation to work together in advancing a cleaner, more connected, and sustainable transport future.

KANZO NAKAI
Director
Transport Sector Office
Asian Development Bank

ANOUJ MEHTA
Country Director
Thailand Resident Mission
Asian Development Bank

FOREWORD

In November 2025, the Cabinet approved Thailand's Nationally Determined Contribution 3.0, marking a significant strengthening of our national climate commitments. Under this update, Thailand now targets a 47% reduction in greenhouse gas emissions by 2035 (from 2019 levels) and aims to achieve net-zero emissions by 2050. These enhanced targets reflect our determination to pursue a low-carbon development pathway. The transport sector will play a major role in meeting these goals, as road transport moves about 80% of people and goods and remains a major source of emissions.

In recent years, Thailand has made meaningful progress in advancing this agenda. We have strengthened our national electric vehicle (EV) policy framework through the adoption of the 30@30 target and the subsequent EV 3.0 and EV 3.5 incentive packages, expanded early efforts to introduce electric buses in urban and intercity services, broadened domestic EV manufacturing capacity, and seen steady growth in the national charging network. These initiatives form an important foundation for enhancing energy security, strengthening industrial competitiveness, and improving mobility for our citizens.

This *Policy Assessment and Action Plan 2025–2035*, undertaken by the Asian Development Bank at the request of the Office of Transport and Traffic Policy and Planning, and refined through extensive consultation with Thai agencies, provides the analytical depth and structured implementation pathway required for the next phase of Thailand's e-mobility transition. The report presents clear sequencing of priority actions, recommends suitable financing and institutional arrangements, and outlines monitoring and coordination mechanisms that can support effective implementation. These insights will help us align Thailand's enhanced climate commitments with practical transport policies and investment pipelines across the sector.

Looking ahead, the Office of Transport and Traffic Policy and Planning will continue working closely with relevant ministries, provincial authorities, the private sector, and development partners to advance Thailand's transport sector transformation that delivers sustained economic, environmental, and social benefits for the country.

JIRAROTH SUKOLRAT
Director General
Office of Transport and Traffic Policy and Planning
Ministry of Transport, Thailand

ABOUT THIS REPORT, THE AUTHORS, AND METHODOLOGY

This report was financed by the Asian Development Bank (ADB) regional technical assistance *Accelerating Climate Transitions Through Green Finance in Southeast Asia* (TA-6983 REG) with funding support from the United Kingdom–Association of Southeast Asian Nations Catalytic Green Finance Facility Trust Fund (UK-ACGF). Additional support was provided through the technical assistance *Strengthening the Bio-Circular-Green Economy* (TA-10079) funded by ADB, the Australian Government's Department of Foreign Affairs and Trade, the Republic of Korea e-Asia and Knowledge Partnership Fund, and the OPEC Fund for International Development (OPEC Fund).

This report was written by Shailendra Kaushik, co-founder of the Cities Forum and ACGF consultant, with inputs from Arun Ramamurthy, principal transport Specialist, ADB Transport Sector Group; Rodrigo Martinez, senior infrastructure finance specialist, ADB Southeast Asia Green Finance Hub; and Sree Kartha, ACGF consultant. We gratefully acknowledge the technical contributions of Jürg Grütter, chief executive officer, Grütter Consulting. We also thank our colleagues, including Katherine Guy, senior infrastructure finance specialist, ADB; Rebecca Stapleton, senior transport specialist, ADB; Karan Chouksey, climate change specialist, ADB; and Cheunchanok Jantanalikhit, ACGF consultant, for their peer review. Coordination and production were managed by Albert Graves, ACGF consultant; Criselda Rufino, infrastructure officer, ADB; and Ann Mushayt Alemania, operations officer, ADB. The report was designed by Rocilyn Locsin Laccay; edited by Lawrence Casiraya; proofread by Jess Macasaet; and page-proofed by Maricelle Abellar.

Special recognition is made to Kanzo Nakai, director, ADB Transport Sector Office; Anouj Mehta, country director, ADB Thailand Resident Mission; and Scott Roberts, head, ADB Southeast Asia Green Finance Hub for their guidance in developing this report. The report's methodology is structured in three stages: assess, develop, and recommend. "Assess" initiates with a situational analysis, covering transport demand growth, electric vehicle adoption rates, charging infrastructure, and production capacities. "Develop" then identifies challenges along with infrastructure needs, benchmarking 10 economies as case studies. "Recommend" concludes with a strategic action plan, policy measures, and a robust implementation framework.

To evaluate future infrastructure scaling, three scenarios are presented—as is, global average, and optimistic—with expected outcomes depending on progress, from slow infrastructure expansion to rapid growth in charging stations.

A Strengths, Weaknesses, Opportunities, and Threats (SWOT) analysis breaks down the key factors that will shape the success of the e-mobility transition, including strong government support, rapid market growth, and potential for local production (Strengths); insufficient charging infrastructure, uneven vehicle segment growth, and limited renewable energy integration (Weaknesses); the government's push for carbon neutrality as well as innovations (Opportunities); and reliance on outdated charging standards and heavy dependence on fossil fuels (Threats).

This multifaceted approach enables the report to tailor its recommendations. It puts forward practical solutions under the proposed Thailand E-Mobility Mission 2025–2035 to accelerate a green, resilient, and inclusive e-mobility shift.

ABBREVIATIONS

AC	alternating current
ADB	Asian Development Bank
ASEAN	Association of Southeast Asian Nations
BEV	battery electric vehicle
BMTA	Bangkok Mass Transit Authority
BOI	Board of Investment
CAGR	compound annual growth rate
DC	direct current
DC CCS2	Direct Current Combined Charging System 2
DC CHAdeMO	Direct Current CHArge de MOve
EV	electric vehicle*
EVAT	Electric Vehicle Association of Thailand
EVCI	electric vehicle charging infrastructure
EVSE	electric vehicle supply equipment
FCV	fuel cell vehicle
GHG	greenhouse gas
GW	gigawatt
HEV	hybrid electric vehicle
ICE	internal combustion engine
kW	kilowatt
kWh	kilowatt-hour
M&E	monitoring and evaluation
MOF	Ministry of Finance
NDC	nationally determined contribution
NEV	new energy vehicle
OTP	Office of Transport and Traffic Policy and Planning
PHEV	plug-in hybrid electric vehicle
PPP	public–private partnership
R&D	research and development
TCL	Transport Company Limited
V2G	vehicle-to-grid
ZEV	zero-emission vehicle

* These are vehicles powered either entirely or partially by electricity, utilizing an e-motor instead of a traditional internal combustion engine. For the purposes of this report, the term "EVs" encompasses all three primary types: battery e-vehicles, hybrid e-vehicles, and plug-in hybrid e-vehicles.

EXECUTIVE SUMMARY

This report focuses on advancing Thailand's transition to sustainable transport through e-mobility investments and policy development. The study provides a comprehensive policy and investment road map to accelerate the electrification of urban and intercity mobility, strengthen infrastructure readiness, and position Thailand as a regional hub for future mobility technologies.

Building on this policy assessment, the report recommends launching the Thailand E-Mobility Mission 2025–2035, which outlines a comprehensive framework to drive the country's transition toward clean transport. The mission aligns with Thailand's long-term climate goals, and establishes the foundation for a modern, inclusive, and resilient transport system that supports net-zero emissions by 2050.

It also identifies three specific key potential investment areas: urban electric buses (e-buses) for Bangkok in collaboration with the Bangkok Mass Transit Authority (BMTA); intercity e-buses with the Transport Company Limited; and interurban and urban e-buses in provinces such as Phuket and Chonburi.

The policy assessment and action plan build on a detailed sector assessment and analysis.

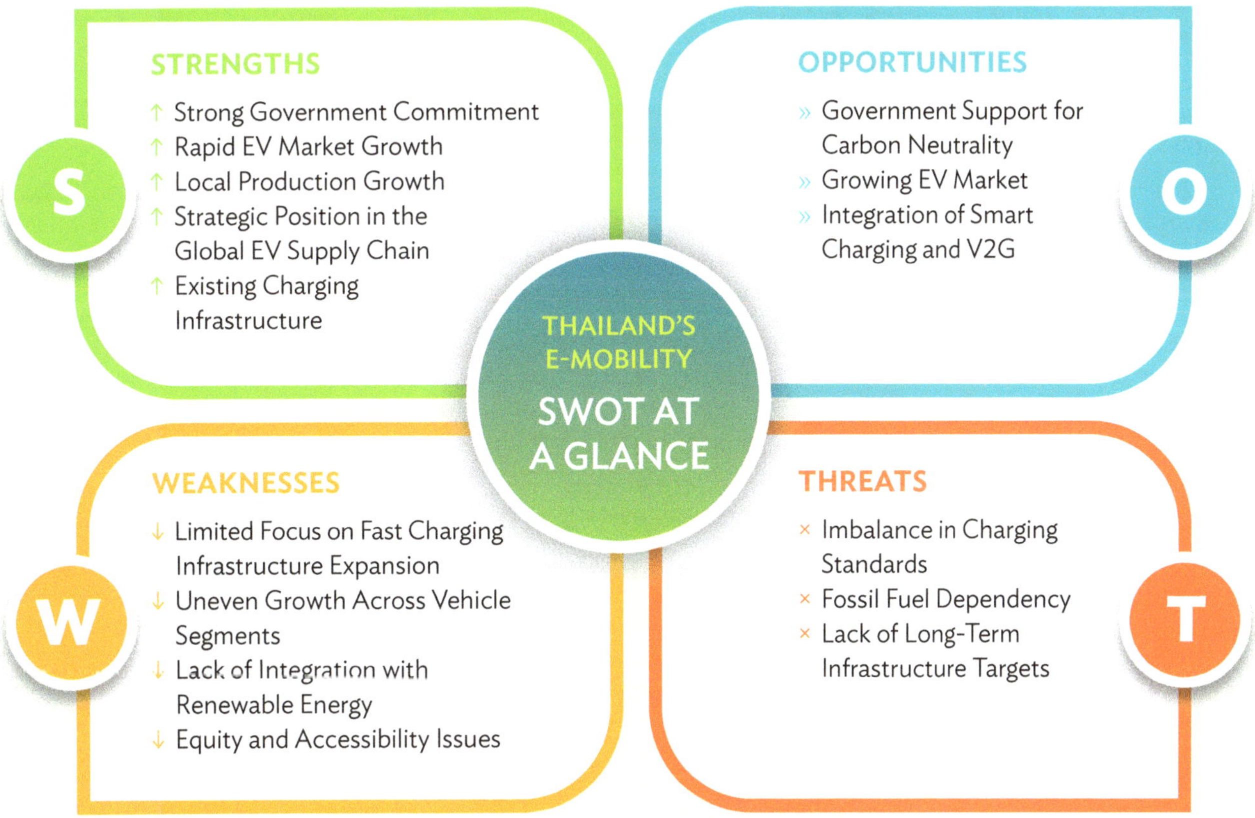

POLICY DRIVERS FOR THAILAND'S E-MOBILITY TRANSITION

The action plan identifies 10 policy drivers across demand, supply, and infrastructure to guide Thailand's shift to clean mobility. These drivers address current challenges and opportunities, and align with the proposed Thailand E-Mobility Mission 2025–2035. Together, they provide the foundation for 50 specific measures detailed in the report, covering the full spectrum of market development, manufacturing, and infrastructure needs.

POLICY DRIVERS

DEMAND SIDE

1. Market Development and Consumer Incentives
2. Consumer Awareness and Communication
3. Demand Assessment and Aggregation

SUPPLY SIDE

4. Tax Incentives
5. Vehicle Emission and Clean-Fuel Standards
6. Targets and Mandates
7. Research Development and Capacity Building

INFRASTRUCTURE SIDE

8. User-Centric Charging Infrastructure
9. Codes and Standards
10. Funding Resources and Institutional Setup

The mission is underpinned by four strategic programs:

STRATEGIC PROGRAMS

1 Public Transport and Freight Sector Electrification

Decarbonizing high-impact segments through e-bus and e-truck deployment

2 National EV Charging Deployment

Ensuring accessibility, interoperability, and reliability across the country

3 Domestic EV Manufacturing

Fostering domestic innovation and industrial competitiveness

4 National EV Skilling and Capacity Building

Developing a skilled workforce and strengthening institutional readiness

Together, these programs are built on an integrated policy, investment, and institutional framework to advance sustainable mobility in Thailand.

INFRASTRUCTURE SCALING SCENARIOS

To guide planning for Thailand's zero-emission vehicle (ZEV) charging network, three growth pathways illustrate how different levels of infrastructure investment could shape the user experience and adoption pace.

1. As-Is	2. Global Average	3. Optimistic
18 ZEVs per charging station (24, including battery electric vehicles and plug-in hybrid electric vehicles), reflecting the current or minimal development level, where charging infrastructure grows at a current pace compared to EV adoption. A conservative approach that may present challenges for EV users.	11 ZEVs per charging station, representing a moderate increase in charging infrastructure to better support EV users and reduce potential bottlenecks. A balanced and realistic approach that ensures user convenience and promotes adoption.	8 ZEVs per charging station, demonstrating a significant ramp-up in charging infrastructure to ensure widespread accessibility and convenience for EV owners. An ambitious approach that fosters confidence in the EV ecosystem and drives higher adoption rates.

PHASING PLAN: THAILAND E-MOBILITY MISSION 2025–2035

Thailand's e-mobility transition is designed to unfold in three phases, moving from foundation building to national scaling and long-term sustainability. Each phase builds on the previous one, aligning policy, infrastructure, and industry growth to achieve full electrification of public transport and freight by 2035.

2025–2027: Foundation Building

Consumer subsidies, manufacturer tax exemptions, e-bus fleet integration, charging hubs for freight, fast-charging corridors between cities, financial support for battery and component production, and training programs for technicians and engineers.

2028–2032: Expansion and Scaling

Stronger emissions regulations, expanded recycling infrastructure, e-bus deployment in regional and intercity routes, freight electrification for long-haul logistics, charging access expansion in semi-urban and rural areas, domestic manufacturing scaling to 30% localization, and large-scale training programs to build national EV capacity.

2033–2035: Maturity and Sustainability

Fully electrified public transit in key cities; zero-emission freight; nationwide charging coverage; smart-grid technology integration; and advanced workforce development in battery recycling, software, and smart charging to support a competitive EV industry.

NEXT STEPS

Successful implementation of Thailand's E-Mobility Action Plan will require a coordinated, phased approach. The following immediate priorities outline the next steps to operationalize the road map.

1. **Engage partners and key stakeholders.** Consult with government agencies, private sector actors, and financial institutions to gather feedback, refine proposed measures, and ensure alignment and buy-in for implementation.

2. **Develop actionable implementation plans.** Translate each policy intervention into detailed, time-bound plans with clear resource requirements, institutional responsibilities, and accountability mechanisms.

3. **Scale pilot projects and phase implementation.** Prioritize high-impact interventions such as EV charging infrastructure deployment and public transport electrification in the initial phase. Use pilot projects to test approaches and scale successful models nationwide.

4. **Build capacity and strengthen collaboration.** Launch targeted training and knowledge programs for government and private stakeholders. Foster partnerships to accelerate investments in charging networks, e-bus systems, and green logistics.

5. **Ensure policy and financial readiness.** Strengthen policy frameworks, including fiscal incentives, carbon pricing, and regulatory measures, to encourage private sector participation. Align the action plan with Thailand's Nationally Determined Contribution and net-zero commitments, and mobilize international climate finance through mechanisms such as the Green Climate Fund and Climate Investment Funds.

I. OVERVIEW OF E-MOBILITY IN THAILAND

Thailand is at a critical phase in its transition toward a sustainable, low-carbon economy. The transport sector, one of the largest contributors to national greenhouse gas (GHG) emissions, stands at the center of this transformation. As a signatory to the Paris Agreement, Thailand has committed to reducing its GHG emissions by 30% unconditionally and up to 40% conditionally by 2030, with the goal of achieving net-zero emissions by 2050. The country has made significant progress since achieving upper middle-income status in 2011, supported by strong Sustainable Development Goal (SDG) rankings and a high human development index. Nevertheless, persistent challenges such as income inequality, labor shortages, environmental degradation, and gaps in administrative efficiency continue to hinder its inclusive growth. Thailand's 13th National Economic and Social Development Plan (2023–2027) emphasizes creating a value-based economy, promoting environmental sustainability, enhancing human capital, and improving public sector efficiency to support the country's ambition of attaining high-income status.

ELECTRIC VEHICLES, CHARGING INFRASTRUCTURE, AND PRODUCTION CAPACITIES

Thailand's transport sector is experiencing rapid growth in vehicle ownership and a gradual shift toward electrification. By 2035, vehicle registrations are projected to reach 68.2 million, and with further growth, the motorization rate is estimated to reach 886 vehicles per 1,000 people by 2050. As of November 2024, the country had 46.9 million vehicles (Figure 1), mainly passenger cars and motorcycles, with road transport handling 80% of freight and passenger movement. The electric vehicle (EV) market is expanding rapidly but unevenly across segments.

In 2024, EV registrations stood at 700,000, accounting for 1.5% of the total vehicle stock. Battery electric vehicles (BEVs) have shown exceptional growth with a compound annual growth rate (CAGR) of 143.6% since 2020, while hybrid electric vehicles (HEVs) and plug-in hybrid electric vehicles (PHEVs) grew at 28.2% and 25.7%, respectively. Thailand's EV 3.0 policy targets the production of 3.04 million zero-emission vehicles (ZEVs) by 2035—an ambitious plan that may prove challenging, particularly for slower-moving segments such as tuktuks, buses, and trucks.

Thailand has made notable progress in positioning itself as a regional hub for EV production, supported by the government's targets under the National EV Roadmap, which aims for 30% of all vehicles produced domestically to be electric by 2030. However, EV adoption among consumers remains limited, constrained by high up-front costs and insufficient charging infrastructure. To address these challenges, the government is expanding the national charging network and providing targeted financial incentives. In parallel, Thailand's Bio-Circular-Green strategy emphasizes the development of sustainable transport systems, the promotion of EVs, and the expansion of public transport networks.

EXISTING AND PROJECTED GROWTH IN TRANSPORT

Thailand's mobility sector plays a significant role in driving economic growth by supporting trade, tourism, and both regional and urban connectivity. As a major logistics hub in Southeast Asia, the country relies heavily on its transport infrastructure to link economic zones, urban and rural areas, and facilitate access to global markets. In 2022, the sector contributed 4.9% to the national gross domestic product, underscoring its vital role in domestic and international supply chains.[1]

1 A. Verkehrswende. 2024. *Towards Decarbonising Transport: Thailand 2024 – A Stocktake on Sectoral Ambition.* https://thai-german-cooperation.info/wp-content/uploads/2024/04/EN-Towards-Decarbonising-Transport-Thailand-2024_A-Stocktake-on-Sectoral-Ambition.pdf.

Figure 1: Accumulated Vehicle Registrations in Thailand
(million)

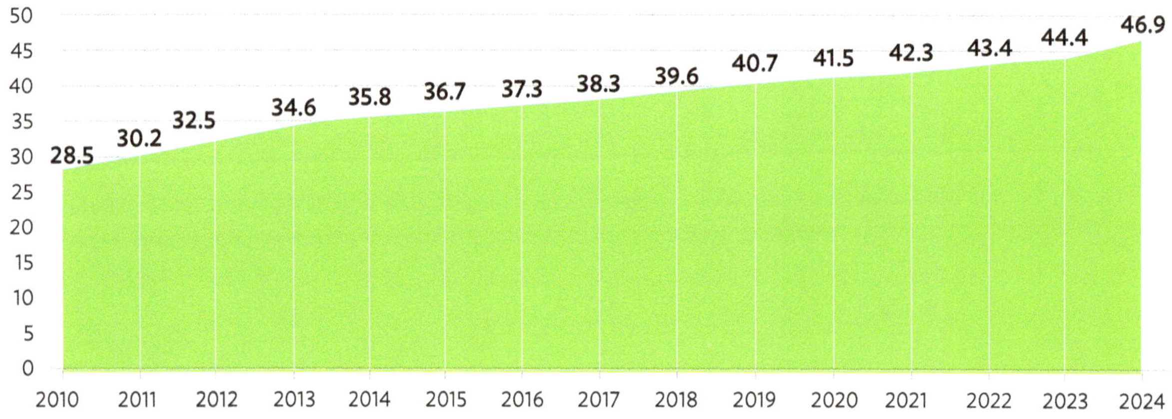

Source: ACGF.

Road transport dominates the nation's mobility sector, accounting for around 80% of freight and passenger movements, most of which rely on internal combustion engine (ICE) vehicles.[2] As of November 2024, Thailand had 46.8 million registered vehicles, with an estimated motorization rate of 642 vehicles, up from 596 vehicles in 2022.[3]

Vehicle distribution in Thailand is heavily dominated by passenger cars and motorcycles, which together account for nearly 95% of the national vehicle stock. Of the total, motorcycles represent 52.2%, passenger cars 42.6%, trucks 2.8%, buses 0.3%, and tuktuks 0.04% (Figure 2).

Since 2008, vehicle registrations across all segments have grown with a CAGR of 3.7%. Passenger cars have experienced the highest growth rate at 5.2%,[4] followed by trucks (3.3%)[5] and motorcycles (2.5%).[6]

Tuktuk registrations have declined at a rate of 0.3%, according to the Electric Vehicle Association of Thailand (EVAT), largely due to complex registration processes and regional restrictions.[7] Similarly, both private and public buses have recorded limited growth of 1.1% since 2010,[8] leading to delays in fleet replacement and the continued operation of aging vehicles.[9] There are 0.8 public buses per 1,000 population in Thailand, ranking second in the Association of Southeast Asian Nations (ASEAN) region after Singapore (Figure 3).

2 O. Buthphorm, V. Sukhotu, and T. Hengsadeekul. 2024. An Analysis of the Development Factors of Rail Freight Transport in Thailand: A Structural Equation Modelling Approach. *Infrastructures*. 9(7), 102. https://doi.org/10.3390/infrastructures9070102.

3 Department of Land Transport. Annual Registration Statistics. https://web.dlt.go.th/statistics; Asian Transport Outlook. 2024. Thailand Transport Climate Profile. https://asiantransportoutlook.com/documents/154/Thailand-climate-profile.pdf; World Health Organization.Data - Thailand. https://data.who.int/countries/764; ASEANStats Data Portal. Total number of registered road motor vehicles. https://data.aseanstats.org/indicator/ASE.TRP.ROD.B.005.

4 ASEANStats Data Portal. Number of registered passenger cars. https://data.aseanstats.org/indicator/ASE.TRP.ROD.B.006.

5 ASEANStats Data Portal. Number of registered trucks. https://data.aseanstats.org/indicator/ASE.TRP.ROD.B.008.

6 ASEANStats Data Portal. Total number of registered motorcycles. https://data.aseanstats.org/indicator/ASE.TRP.ROD.B.011.

7 *Bangkok Post*. 2019. https://bangkokpost.com/business/motoring/1674980/ev-group-urges-changes-to-3-wheeler-laws.

8 Department of Land Transport. Annual Registration Statistics. https://web.dlt.go.th/statistics.

9 ESCAP. 2023. *Study Report on Transitioning to Electric Public Buses in Thailand*. https://unescap.org/sites/default/d8files/event-documents/ESCAP-2022-RP-Transitioning-to-Electric-Public-Buses-Thailand%20%281%29.pdf.

Figure 2: **Share of Registered Vehicles by Segment** (as of November 2024)

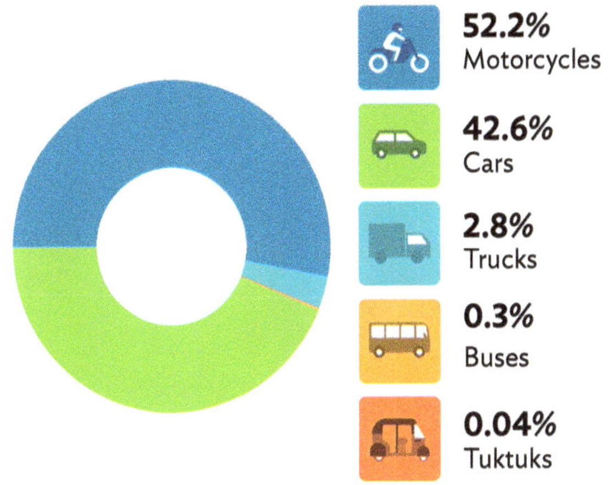

Source: ACGF.

Assuming the current CAGR continues through 2035, Thailand is projected to have 57 million registered vehicles by 2030 and 68.2 million by 2035 (Figure 4). The motorization rate is set to grow to 886 vehicles per 1,000 population by 2050.[10] This rapid growth underscores the need for a well- informed strategy and robust policy framework to mitigate environmental impacts. The plan should prioritize clean modes of transport, effective travel demand management, and the promotion of shared and public transport systems.

Figure 3: Public Buses per 1,000 Population in ASEAN Countries, 2023

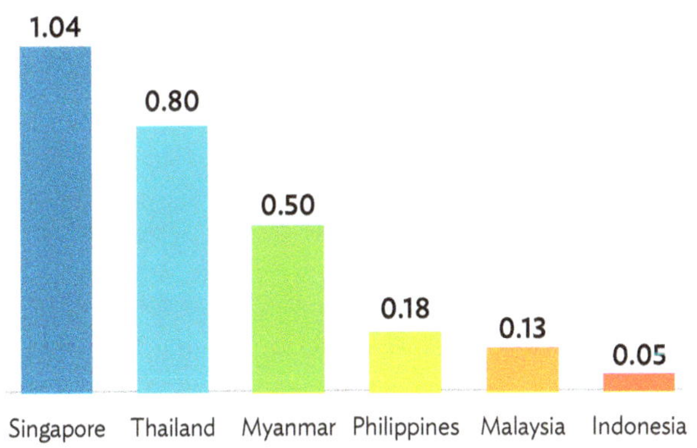

ASEAN = Association of Southeast Asian Nations.
Source: ACGF.

Figure 4: Projected Vehicle Growth in Thailand (million)

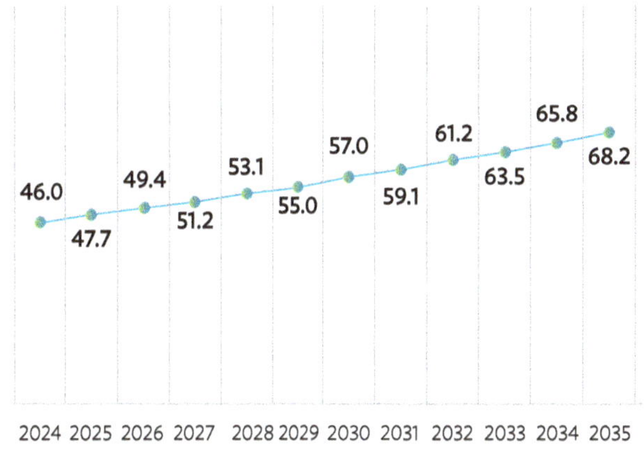

Source: ACGF.

EXISTING AND PROJECTED GROWTH FOR ELECTRIC VEHICLES

As of 2024, Thailand had a total of 700,000 accumulated EV registrations, accounting for 1.5% of all registered vehicles.[11] In terms of vehicle types, passenger cars dominate EV adoption, representing 90% of registered EVs, followed by motorcycles (9.4%) and buses (0.4%). Trucks and tuktuks each contribute 0.1% of the total. The distribution of EV technologies also varies by segment (Figure 5). As of August 2024, all registered PHEVs were passenger cars. Among HEVs, 97.9% were cars and 2.1% were motorcycles. For BEVs, 60.9% were cars, 28% motorcycles, 0.5% tuktuks, 1.3% buses, and 0.3% trucks.

Figure 5: Share of EVs Registered in Thailand (as of August 2024)

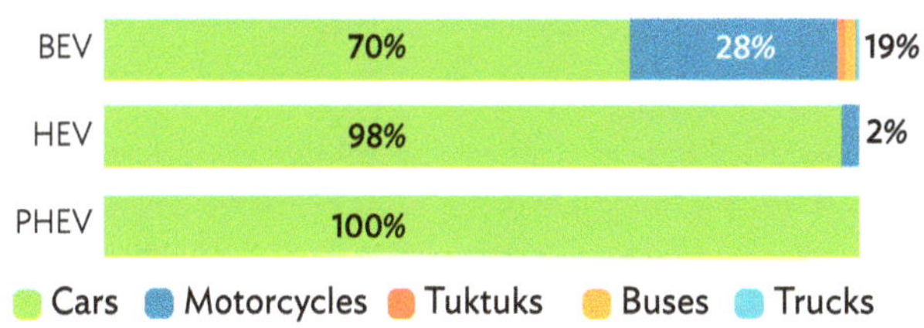

BEV = battery electric vehicle, EV = electric vehicle, HEV = hybrid electric vehicle, PHEV = plug-in hybrid electric vehicle.
Source: ACGF.

[10] Asian Transport Outlook. 2023. Thailand Country Profile. https://asiantransportobservatory.org/documents/65/Thailand_20231002.pdf.
[11] 2024 data is up to August 2024.

Figure 6: Growth of EV Registrations, 2020–2024
('000)

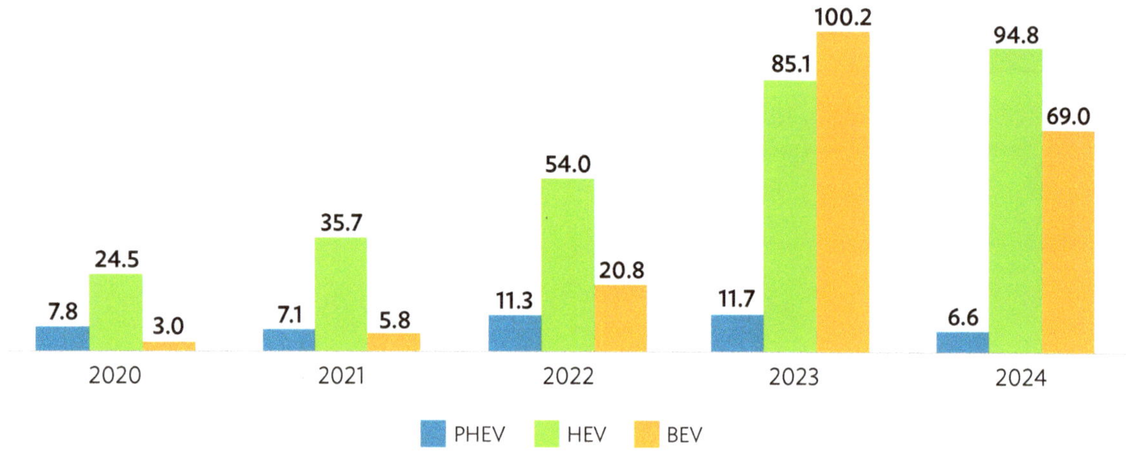

BEV = battery electric vehicle, EV = electric vehicle, HEV = hybrid electric vehicle, PHEV = plug-in hybrid electric vehicle.
Source: EVAT. 2024. https://evat.or.th/images/evinfo/current-status/2024-09/Poster_HEV%20PHEV%20BEV_2024%20Aug%2031_THEN.png.

Thailand's adoption of EVs has been driven by supportive government policies over more than a decade, evolving through three phases: the initial kickoff, the EV 3.0 policy introduced in 2022, and the EV 3.5 policy launched in 2024.

Thailand's policy-driven transition to e-mobility has been led by HEVs, which dominate the current EV landscape (Figure 6). HEVs account for 62.7% of the total EV stock, with over 400,000 registrations as of August 2024. Of these, 200,000 HEVs were registered between 2020 and 2024, and another 200,000 prior to 2020.

BEVs are the next most prominent category, representing 28.7% of the EV stock (equivalent to 0.43% of total vehicle stock) with more than 200,000 registrations. As of August 2024, 68,960 BEVs were sold, comprising mostly of passenger cars, followed by motorcycles, trucks, and tuktuks. PHEVs make up 8.6% of the EV stock, totaling approximately 60,000 registrations.[12] These figures highlight the continued dominance of hybrid technologies alongside the growing market penetration of BEVs.

In terms of growth performance, accumulated EV registrations have increased at a CAGR of 38.1% since 2020. Growth rates differ across segments, with BEVs expanding the fastest at 143.6%, followed by HEVs (28.2%) and PHEVs (25.7%).

Under the EV 3.0 policy, the government has set an ambitious target for 30% of all vehicles produced domestically to be electric by 2030. Segment-specific targets have been established to track progress toward a ZEV transition (Table 1). By 2025, the government aims to electrify 225,000 passenger cars, 360,000 motorcycles, 18,000 buses, and 500 tuktuks, totaling 603,500 ZEVs. These targets increase to approximately 1.13 million ZEVs by 2030 and 3.04 million by 2035.

[12] EVAT. Policy Summary. https://thailand-energy-academy.org/assets/upload/coursedocument/file/E112%20Part%201%20EV%20Energy%20Transition%201.pdf.

When considering the domestic sales targets set by the government across the milestone year 2035, motorcycles represent the largest share of total ZEVs at 59.2% (Figure 7). This is followed by cars (37.9%), buses and trucks (2.7%), and tuktuks (0.09%).

Table 1: ZEV Domestic Sales and Production Targets for 2025, 2030, and 2035

Target	Classification	Volume of ZEVs (Year)		
		2025	2030	2035
ZEV Domestic Sales (% of Total Sales)	Passenger Cars/Pickups	225,000 (30%)	440,000 (50%)	1,154,000 (100%)
	Motorcycles	360,000 (20%)	650,000 (40%)	1,800,000 (100%)
	Buses/Trucks	18,000 (20%)	33,000 (35%)	83,000 (100%)
	3-Wheelers (Tuktuks)	500 (85%)	2,000 (100%)	2,800 (100%)
	E-boats	130 (12%)	480 (35%)	1,800 (100%)
Total		**603,630**	**1,125,480**	**3,041,600**
ZEV Production (% of Total Production)	Passenger Cars/Pickups	225,000 (10%)	725,000 (30%)	1,350,000 (50%)
	Motorcycles	360,000 (20%)	675,000 (30%)	1,850,000 (70%)
	Buses/Trucks	18,000 (35%)	34,000 (50%)	84,000 (85%)
	3-Wheelers (Tuktuks)	500 (85%)	2,200 (100%)	2,800 (100%)
	E-boats	130 (12%)	480 (35%)	1,800 (100%)
Total		**603,630**	**1,436,680**	**3,286,800**

ZEV = zero-emission vehicle.
Source: EVAT. Policy Summary. https://thailand-energy-academy.org/assets/upload/coursedocument/file/E112%20Part%201%20EV%20Energy%20Transition%201.pdf.

Figure 7: Distribution of Domestic Sales as per Government Targets, by Segment

Source: EVAT.

Achieving these targets will require substantial year-on-year growth, underscoring the need for a detailed feasibility analysis and action plan. The e-car segment has demonstrated strong growth, with a CAGR of 158.4% between 2022 and 2024 (Figure 8). To meet the 2030 target of 44,000 registrations, an annual CAGR of 37.7% will be required, while achieving the 2035 target of 1.15 million registrations will necessitate a CAGR of 30%. These projections suggest that the 2030 and 2035 targets for the e-car segment are realistically attainable if the current growth trajectory continues.

The e-motorcycle segment recorded an annual CAGR of 53.5% between 2022 and 2024 (Figure 9). Achieving the 2030 target of 650,000 registrations will require an accelerated CAGR of 74.1%, or 38.3% higher than the observed rate. In contrast, the 2035 target of 1.8 million registrations will require a CAGR of 48.4%. This indicates that while the 2035 target is attainable if existing growth trends continue, additional measures will be needed to meet the 2030 target. Typically, new technologies follow an S-curve diffusion pattern, with slow growth in the early stages as markets test new solutions, followed by rapid adoption once a tipping point, often around 5% of sales, is reached.

Figure 8: Projected Growth of E-car Segment as per Government Targets

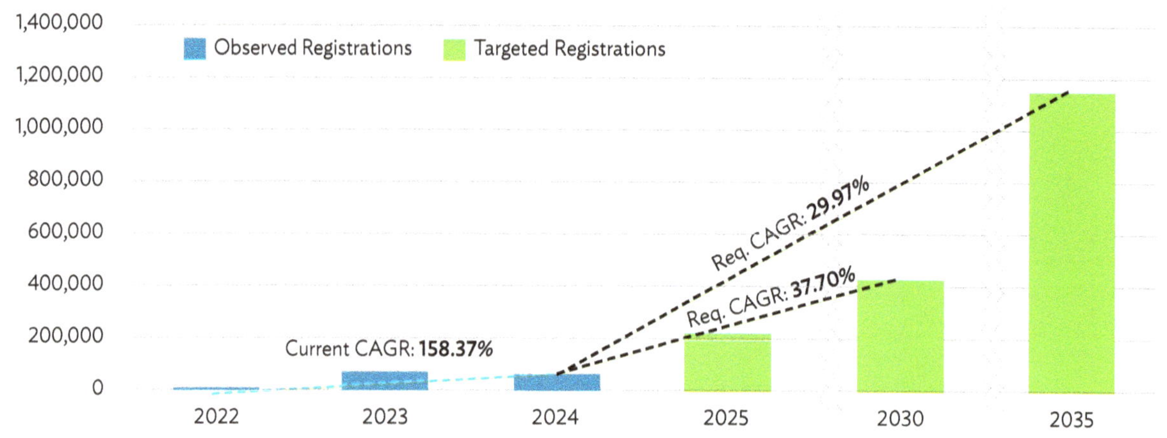

CAGR = compound annual growth rate.
Source: EVAT.

Figure 9: Projected Growth of E-motorcycle Segment as per Government Targets

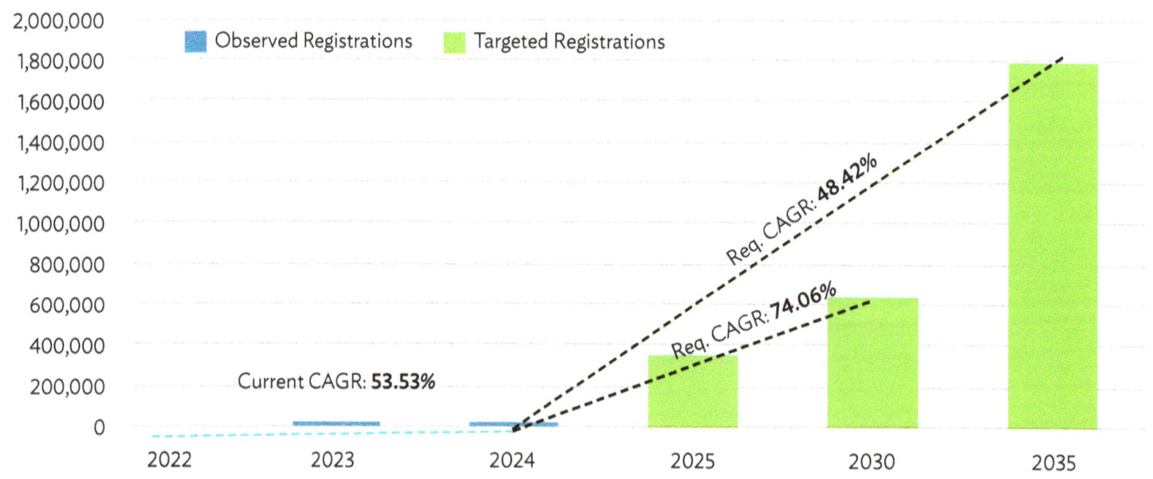

CAGR = compound annual growth rate.
Source: EVAT.

The tuktuk segment has recorded a decline, with a CAGR of –19.8% between 2022 and 2024 (Figure 10). To achieve the 2030 target of 2,200 registrations, the segment will need to achieve a turnaround to reach a CAGR of 57.2%. Similarly, achieving the 2035 target of 2,800 registrations will require a CAGR of 30.8%. As only 47.6% of tuktuks were electric as of 2024, targeted government support will be essential to accelerate electrification in this segment.

The government has combined the e-bus and e-truck segments to establish common targets for 2030 and 2035 (Figure 11). Between 2022 and 2024, the combined segment recorded negative sales growth. Achieving the 2030 target will require a market-driven approach to accelerate adoption rapidly, while meeting the 2035 target will demand a more comprehensive strategy to address existing challenges, reverse the decline, and sustain momentum.

Achieving Thailand's 2030 and 2035 EV targets will require focused, segment-specific strategies. While e-cars and e-motorcycles are broadly on track, the e-tuktuk and e-bus/e-truck segments need urgent policy support and infrastructure investment to drive electrification.

Figure 10: Projected Growth of E-tuktuk Segment as per Government Targets

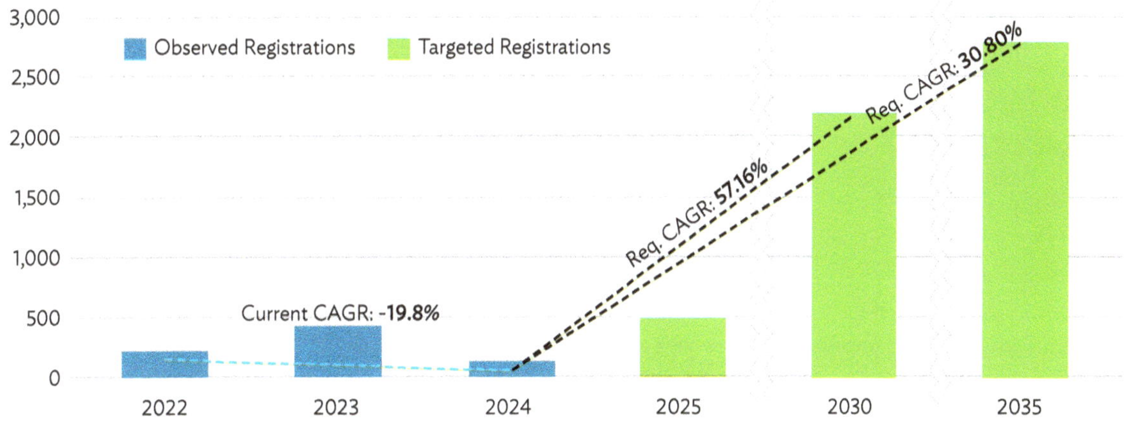

CAGR = compound annual growth rate.
Source: EVAT.

Figure 11: Projected Growth of E-bus/E-truck Segment as per Government Targets

CAGR = compound annual growth rate.
Source: EVAT.

Table 2: Charging Infrastructure Providers and Charger Types in Thailand (as of August 2024)

Locations	DC CCS2	DC CHAdeMO	AC Type 2	Total
3,175	5,039	419	5,388	10,846

AC Type 2 = Alternating Current Type 2, DC CCS2 = Direct Current Combined Charging System 2, CHAdeMO = CHArge de MOve.
Source: EVAT.

Table 3: Charging Infrastructure Available Capacities in Thailand

Charger Type	DC CCS2		DC CHAdeMO		AC Type 2	
Lowest and Highest Available Capacity (in kW)	120	180	60	150	7	22
Average Capacity (in kW)	150		105		14.5	

AC Type 2 = Alternating Current Type 2, DC CCS = Direct Current Combined Charging System 2, CHAdeMO = CHArge de MOve, kW = kilowatt.
Source: EVAT.

CHARGING INFRASTRUCTURE

According to EVAT, as of August 2024 there are 10,846 EV charging outlets at 3,175 locations nationwide, including 5,388 slow chargers and 5,458 fast chargers (Table 2). The current ratio is 24 EVs per charging outlet. When focusing solely on BEVs, the ratio improves to 18 BEVs per outlet, more favorable than the global average of BEVs per public charging point,[15] indicating relatively favorable infrastructure support for fully electric vehicles compared to the other markets.

In Thailand, charger types vary in capacity (kilowatts [kW]) based on whether they are fast or slow chargers (Table 3). Direct Current Combined Charging System 2 (DC CCS2) chargers typically range from 120 kW to 180 kW, while DC CHArge de MOve (DC CHAdeMO) chargers range from 60 kW to 150 kW. Alternating Current (AC) Type 2 chargers operate between 7 kW and 22 kW. Higher-capacity chargers support fast-charging infrastructure, while lower-capacity chargers constitute the slow-charging network.

While Thailand's charging network is almost equally split between DC CCS2 and AC Type 2 systems, policies on charging infrastructure—covering speed, location, and typology—play an important role in improving network density and aligning charger distribution with future EV targets. The introduction of higher-capacity chargers could further enhance efficiency for e-buses and e-trucks.

PRODUCTION CAPACITIES

BEV production in Thailand remains at a nascent stage. As BEVs are a relatively new segment, the market initially depended on imports to meet demand. In 2023, companies receiving EV investment support produced only 164 BEVs.[13] However, further government incentive measures have accelerated BEV adoption, attracting manufacturers to invest in local production. By May 2024, the Thailand Automotive Industry reported that 14 passenger BEV manufacturers, 2 commercial EV manufacturers, and 5 e-bus/e-truck producers had established or were in the process of setting up production lines in Thailand. As a result, the country's domestic BEV production capacity is expected to reach about 600,000 units annually, with new production commencing in 2024 and 2025.[14]

The composition of Thailand's auto market is undergoing a significant shift. In 2023, four BEV manufacturers based in the People's Republic of China (PRC) ranked among the top 10 auto brands in the country, accounting for 21.9% of total sales, up from two manufacturers in 2021, which held the 4th and 10th positions. As of 2023, PRC brands dominated the domestic passenger BEV market with an 82.4% share, while automakers based in the United States (US) accounted for 11.1%.

[13] S. Choksawatpaisan. 2024. Thailand Industry Outlook 2024–2026: Electric Vehicle Industry. Krungsri Research.
[14] The Nation. 2023. Electric tuk-tuk innovator MuvMi to triple fleet as demand soars. https://www.nationthailand.com/business/corporate/40023998.

As the largest automotive hub in Southeast Asia and the tenth largest globally, Thailand is well positioned to benefit from rising global EV demand. In 2023, the country exported a total of $562 billion worth of EV components, ranking third among exporters to Japan and ninth to the US. Its largest market was the PRC, which accounted for $171 billion in 2023.[15] However, this rapid industrial expansion and domestic EV consumption brings new sustainability challenges. As EV adoption accelerates, effective management of end-of-life batteries will be essential to prevent environmental risks and recover valuable materials such as lithium, cobalt, and nickel. Establishing a robust battery recycling system, supported by clear regulations, safe disposal protocols, and incentives for circular economy practices, will be critical to ensuring sustainability in Thailand's EV ecosystem. Drawing on international examples, such as the PRC's mandatory battery recycling standards and the European Union's Battery Directive, could help guide policy and infrastructure development in this area.

KEY FINDINGS

Thailand's transport sector is undergoing a major transformation. Vehicle registrations have maintained a CAGR of 3.7% since 2008, led by passenger cars at 5.2%. As of November 2024, the vehicle stock reached 46.8 million, dominated by motorcycles (52.2%) and passenger cars (42.6%), reflecting the sector's heavy reliance on road transport, which accounts for 80% of freight and passenger movements.

By 2035, total registrations are projected to reach 68.2 million, with a motorization rate expected to reach 886 vehicles per 1,000 population by 2050.

The EV market continues to expand rapidly but unevenly across segments. By 2024, EV registrations reached 700,000, representing 1.5% of the national vehicle stock. BEVs have recorded the highest CAGR of 143.6% since 2020, while HEVs and PHEVs grew at 28.2% and 25.7%, respectively. Under the EV 3.0 policy, Thailand aims to produce 1.12 million ZEVs by 2030 and 3.04 million by 2035. Achieving these targets will be particularly challenging for tuktuk and bus/truck segments, which require annual growth rates of 57.2% and 84.2%, respectively. These ambitious goals call for targeted policy and market interventions to accelerate adoption across all vehicle categories.

Infrastructure development has advanced alongside market growth, with 10,846 EV charging outlets available nationwide as of 2024, equivalent to 18 BEVs per outlet. Domestic BEV production capacity is projected to reach 600,000 units annually by 2025, supported by 14 manufacturers. Continued scaling will be essential for self-reliance and localized EV production in line with the target defined under the EV30@30 policy. In 2023, EV component exports reached $562 billion, while PRC-based manufacturers captured 82.4% of Thailand's BEV market, emphasizing the country's growing role in the regional and global EV supply chain.

As Thailand moves toward its 2030 and 2035 EV goals, a more balanced and adaptive policy framework will be needed to sustain momentum. Addressing lagging segments, deepening infrastructure coverage, and expanding domestic manufacturing will be key to achieving an inclusive and competitive e-mobility ecosystem.

[15] Tractus-Asia. From Diesel to Electric: Thailand's Transition to an EV Manufacturing Powerhouse. https://tractus-asia.com/blog/thailand-transition-to-ev-manufacturing-powerhouse.

ELECTRIC VEHICLE POLICY

Since 2016, Thailand's EV policy development has progressed through phases, evolving from EV 3.0 to EV 3.5 measures between 2022 and 2024 (Figure 12). EV 3.0 policies focused on stimulating demand through subsidies, tax reductions, and import offset requirements, while EV 3.5 measures emphasize deeper localization, with stricter production offset ratios and reduced subsidies for higher-value EVs. Persistent gaps remain, including limited charging infrastructure, insufficient integration with renewable energy, underdeveloped freight electrification, and the absence of long-term infrastructure targets.

Thailand's ratification of the Paris Agreement in 2016 led to the formulation of its National Energy Plan, which set a clear trajectory for clean energy adoption and aims to achieve net-zero emissions by 2050. Electrifying transport is a central pillar of this strategy, recognized as a key driver for reducing GHG emissions under Thailand's nationally determined contribution (NDC) commitments. Consequently, the government has prioritized EV market expansion as a part of a broader effort to transform the country's automotive industry.

Since 2016, government initiatives have focused on creating an enabling ecosystem for EV adoption through a balanced mix of supply- and demand-side incentives. These include fiscal and non-fiscal support, targeted investments for charging infrastructure, and investment-friendly policies to attract private participation and establish a strong domestic manufacturing base.

PHASE I (2017–2021): KICK-OFF PHASE

Between 2017 and 2021, Thailand's EV market entered its initial establishment phase. Government incentives originally designed for eco-car manufacturers (small, fuel-efficient internal combustion engine [ICE] vehicles) were extended to include EVs. Automakers producing at least 100,000 vehicles annually could count EVs alongside eco-cars to qualify for investment incentives, including 8-year corporate income tax exemptions, a 90% reduction in import duties for auto components, and reduced import duties for plants and machinery. In 2019, applicants for BEV investment support also became eligible for HEV manufacturing schemes, with applications required to be submitted by 31 December 2019.

Figure 12: E-Mobility Transition Timeline in Thailand

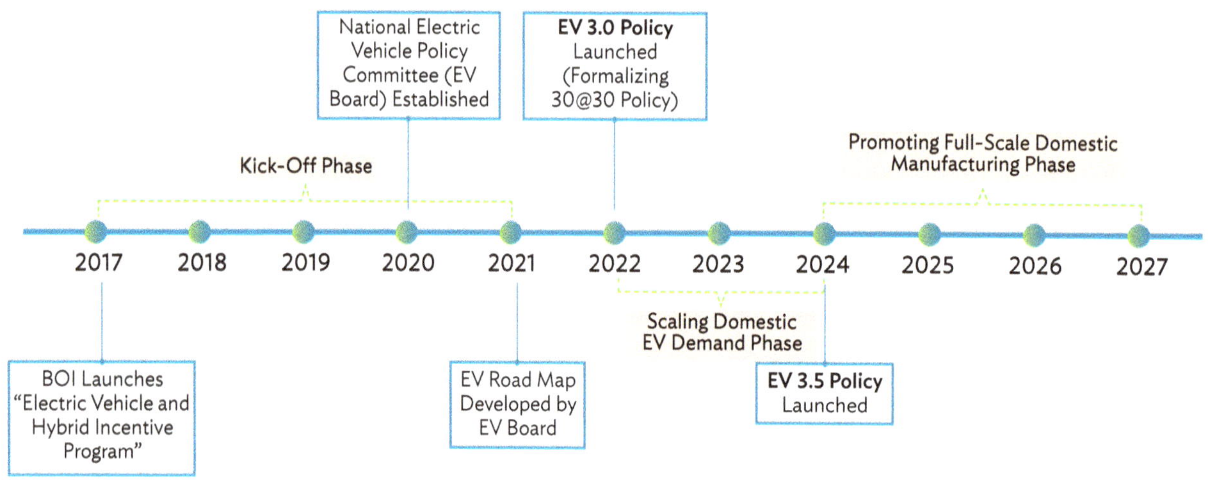

BOI = Board of Investment, EV = electric vehicle.
Source: ACGF.

PHASE II (2022–2023): SCALING DOMESTIC ELECTRIC VEHICLE DEMAND

From 2022, policy emphasis shifted toward expanding domestic production and accelerating market adoption through the EV 3.0 policy. The National E-Vehicle Policy Committee (EV Board) launched strategies to promote ZEVs, formalizing the EV 30@30 policy on 12 May 2021. This policy mandates that by 2030, at least 30% of vehicles manufactured in Thailand must be ZEVs. Interim targets set the share of passenger cars and pickups at 10% of total production and 30% of new registrations by 2025, increasing to 30% and 50%, respectively, by 2030.

The EV 3.0 measures proved highly effective, contributing to the 311% CAGR in new BEV registrations from 32,081 units in 2022 to 131,856 in 2023.[16]

PHASE III (2024–2027): PROMOTING FULL-SCALE DOMESTIC MANUFACTURING CAPABILITIES

Following the success of EV 3.0, the government introduced EV 3.5 to sustain policy momentum and strengthen domestic manufacturing capacity.

The EV 3.5 policy (2024–2027) builds on Thailand's earlier EV 3.0 measures by shifting focus toward local manufacturing and supply chain development. It introduces stricter production offset requirements, reduces incentives for luxury EVs, and extends support to commercial vehicles like e-buses and e-trucks. EV 3.5 also promotes battery recycling, second-life use, and clean energy integration, aiming to strengthen Thailand's role as a regional EV manufacturing hub while advancing its 30@30 and decarbonization targets.

COMPARING ELECTRIC VEHICLE POLICY MEASURES UNDER 3.0 AND 3.5

Thailand's EV policy has progressed from stimulating demand under EV 3.0 to focusing on industrial localization under EV 3.5. While EV 3.0 emphasized investment promotion, purchase subsidies, and import offset-linked incentives to kick-start local production, EV 3.5 shifts toward long-term sustainability and competitiveness. It introduces stricter local production requirements and reduced subsidies, marking a strategic move toward building a fully localized EV manufacturing ecosystem and resilient supply chains to support sustained market growth.

Table 4: Key Highlights of EV 3.0 and EV 3.5 Policy Measures

Policy Measure	EV 3.0 (2022–2024)	EV 3.5 (2024–2027)
Purchase Subsidy	B70,000–B150,000 for passenger BEVs priced ≤ B2 million.	B50,000–100,000 for passenger BEVs priced ≤ B2 million.
	B150,000 for pickups priced ≤ B2 million (≥ 30 kWh battery capacity).	B100,000 for pickups priced ≤ B2 million (≥ 50 kWh battery capacity).
	B18,000 for e-motorcycles.	B10,000 for e-motorcycles.
Excise Tax Reductions	2% for passenger cars (reduced from 8%).	2% for passenger cars during 2024–2025, rising to 8% thereafter.
	0% for pickups (reduced from 10%).	0% for pickups during 2024–2025, rising to 2% thereafter.
	No reduction for motorcycles.	No reduction for motorcycles.
Import Tariff Reductions	Up to 40% for BEVs priced ≤ B2 million.	Up to 40% for BEVs priced ≤ B2 million.
	Up to 20% for BEVs priced ≤ B7 million.	Up to 20% for BEVs priced ≤ B7 million.
	No reduction for motorcycles.	No reduction for motorcycles.
Offset Ratios	1:1 for 2024; 1:1.5 for 2025.	1:2 for 2026; 1:3 for 2027.
	Models priced ≤ B2 million could be offset with any domestic BEV model.	Models priced < B2 million must be offset with identical domestically manufactured models.

continued on next page

[16] EVAT data.

Table 4 *continued*

Policy Measure	EV 3.0 (2022-2024)	EV 3.5 (2024-2027)
Domestic Manufacturing	Encouraged initial domestic production through import offsets.	Strengthened emphasis on scaling local manufacturing with stricter offset ratios.
Charging Infrastructure	5-year tax holidays for stations with ≥ 40 chargers (10 DC), and 3 years for stations with 16–40 chargers.	Continued focus on incentives and joint ventures, with enhanced conditions for charging infrastructure.

BEV = battery electric vehicle, EV = electric vehicle, DC = direct current.
Source: ACGF.

EV 3.0 played a key role in scaling Thailand's EV market by offering purchase subsidies of B70,000–B150,000 for passenger BEVs and additional incentives for pickups and motorcycles (Table 4). Vehicles endorsed by the Board of Investment (BOI) benefited from a reduced 2% excise tax, and import tariffs were cut by up to 40% for BEVs priced at or below B2 million. Import offset rules required manufacturers importing EVs in 2022–2023 to produce equivalent units locally at a 1:1 ratio in 2024 and 1:1.5 in 2025. Charging infrastructure was also incentivized through tax holidays for developers. These measures drove a 311% CAGR in BEV registrations between 2022 and 2023.

With the rollout of EV 3.5, policy emphasis has shifted to industrial localization. Subsidies have been reduced, and stricter offset ratios will apply—1:2 in 2026 and 1:3 in 2027. High-end EVs priced above B2 million must be manufactured locally to qualify. These changes aim to attract long-term investment, strengthen domestic manufacturing, and build a globally competitive EV industry in Thailand.

RECENT DEVELOPMENTS AND AREAS FOR IMPROVEMENT

BMTA and TCL Electrification Plan: As of 2024, the Bangkok Mass Transit Authority (BMTA) operates around 2,900 12-meter buses, half of which is non-air-conditioned and over 30 years old. About 70% of the fleet comprises Euro II diesel buses with an average age of 22 years, while the remaining 30% are compressed-natural-gas-powered Euro III units that are more than 6 years old. A private operator, Thai Smile, has deployed 2,350 battery electric buses as of November 2024. BMTA plans to replace ICE fleet with e-buses in three phases: Phase 1 with 350 buses, Phase 2 with 1,520 buses, and Phase 3 with another 1,520 buses, totaling 3,390 battery electric buses. The Transport Company Limited (TCL), which operates intercity services, manages a fleet of 7,300 buses with an average fleet age of 30 years, and plans to induct 381 e-buses in Phase 1 of its electrification program. These transitions represent a substantial opportunity for scaling domestic e-bus manufacturing and underscore the need for a coordinated national public transport electrification plan.

Production timeframe extension: In response to industry feedback, the government extended the production timeframe for BEVs and introduced additional incentives for HEVs to support the auto sector. Under the current EV incentive package, manufacturers are required to produce one locally manufactured vehicle for each imported vehicle, with offset ratios increasing in subsequent years.[17]

Foreign investment: A major PRC automaker inaugurated its first EV manufacturing factory in Thailand, signaling a milestone for regional EV investment. The facility has an annual production capacity of 150,000 vehicles and reinforces Thailand's appeal and role as a growing EV manufacturing hub in Southeast Asia.[18] Similarly, a leading Japanese automaker announced plans to produce its first BEV, an electric version of its popular D-Max pickup truck, in Thailand,[19] further diversifying the country's EV production base.

[17] Board of Investment. 2024. Thailand EV board approves extended production timeframe for BEV and inclusion of mild HEV in hybrid incentive package to support industry's electrification (Press release). https://osos.boi.go.th/EN/news/2138/Thailand-EV-Board-Approves-Extended Production-Timeframe-for.

[18] BYD. 2024. BYD Thailand factory inauguration and roll-off of its 8 millionth new energy vehicle. https://www.byd.com/za/news-list/BYD-roll-off-of-Its-8-millionth-new-energy-vehicle.

[19] *Reuters*. 2024. Japan's Isuzu Motors to produce EV pickup trucks in Thailand. https://reuters.com/business/autos-transportation/japans-isuzu-motors-produce-ev-pickup-trucks-thailand-2024-03-21.

Made in Thailand initiative: PRC EV manufacturers are rapidly increasing their presence in Thailand's automotive market, which has traditionally been dominated by Japanese firms. In 2023, PRC brands captured 11% of the domestic market, selling approximately 87,000 units.[20] This surge reflects the success of Thailand's pro-investment policies, including subsidies and excise tax reductions for imported BEVs, contingent on the commencement of local assembly by 2024 or 2025. Consequently, BEV sales rose to 74,000 units in 2023, with market share increasing from 1.2% to 9.5% year on year. Beyond the domestic market, PRC manufacturers are positioning Thailand as a production and export base for the ASEAN region, Australia, Europe, and New Zealand, leveraging tariff advantages under the ASEAN-PRC Free Trade Agreement.

Together, these developments illustrate the strong momentum of Thailand's EV production market, driven by responsive policy adjustments, growing foreign direct investment, and rapid expansion in local manufacturing. The extension of production timeframes and new HEV incentives underline the government's commitment to sustaining industry growth. With BEVs now comprising 25.2% of passenger car sales and Thailand emerging as a regional export hub, the country is consolidating its position as a leader in Southeast Asia's e-mobility transformation.

POLICY IMPROVEMENT AREAS

Thailand has shown strong commitment to advancing e-mobility through comprehensive policies such as EV 3.5. However, several areas require further attention to ensure effective implementation and readiness, particularly in strengthening charging infrastructure, supporting balanced market growth across vehicle segments, and enhancing integration with renewable energy systems (Table 5).

Table 5: Identified Gaps in Existing EV Policy Measures: Improvement Areas

Key Challenge	Description	Likely Impact
POLICY AREA 1: **Charging Strategy**		
Limited Focus on Charging Infrastructure Expansion	• While the EV 3.5 package emphasizes subsidies and tax reductions for EV purchases, there is insufficient emphasis on expanding charging infrastructure, especially in rural or underdeveloped regions. • There are no targeted incentives for fast chargers that could facilitate electrifying commercial and public fleets segments, such as buses, taxis, or logistics vehicles.	• Lack of widespread and accessible charging stations may deter EV adoption, particularly in areas outside urban centers.
Review Benefits of Localized Renewable Energy Integration in Targeted Areas and Study Emerging Concept for Renewable Energy Integration	• Integrating renewable energy sources into the charging station at targeted locations could potentially provide scalable and commercially viable alternatives to enhance access to clean energy for EV charging. • This issue can be studied and if there is a potential benefit of using such integration, appropriate policy measures could be adopted.	• Integrating renewable energy with EV charging extends beyond simply co-locating distributed solar plants with charging units. Emerging concepts such as virtual power plants, green open access routes, and renewable energy aggregation provide scalable and commercially viable alternatives to enhance access to clean energy for EV charging. These approaches could be studied further as part of a long-term strategy.

continued on next page

[20] *KrASIA*. 2024. China automakers doubled Thai market share in 2023 on EVs. https://kr-asia.com/china-automakers-doubled-thai-market-share-in-2023-on-evs.

Table 5 *continued*

Key Challenge	Description	Likely Impact
Limited Focus on Smart Charging and V2G Integration	• The policy does not prioritize the adoption of smart charging systems or V2G technology.	• Absence of smart charging and V2G may lead to inefficiencies in energy use and missed opportunities for grid stabilization through EVs.
Unclear Standards for Interoperability	• Limited emphasis on ensuring interoperability between different charging networks and EV brands.	• This could result in fragmented charging networks, causing inconvenience for EV users and limiting seamless charging experiences.
POLICY AREA 2: **Capacity Development**		
Insufficient Cybersecurity Measures	• The regulatory framework does not address cybersecurity measures for the charging network.	• Without robust cybersecurity, the charging infrastructure is vulnerable to hacking, data theft, and operational disruptions.
Delayed Localization Requirements	• The requirement for EV manufacturers to offset imported EVs with domestic production focuses on vehicles, but lacks clear guidelines for localized charger manufacturing or deployment. • Although there is a focus on domestic production of EVs, there is limited incentive to develop localized supply chains for EV components, such as motors, electronics, and chargers.	• This delay may slow the development of a robust domestic ecosystem for charging equipment.
Equity and Accessibility Concerns	• There is no specific strategy to ensure equitable distribution of charging stations across urban and rural areas or to make them accessible to marginalized groups.	• This could create disparities in EV adoption, particularly for low-income or rural populations.
Cross-Cutting Area	The current policies need to be expanded across the following critical areas: • Upskilling and reskilling. • Organization plan for public sector undertakings with changing human resources requirements due to electrification. • Research and development. • Harmonization of standards. • Guidelines for charging infrastructure. • Battery recycling and end-of-life management. • Public awareness and communications. • Public-private partnership framework to attract private investment in public transport electrification. • Monitoring and evaluation.	• The absence of crosscutting measures in Thailand's EV ecosystem hampers progress in electrifying the transport sector and needs to be considered in the next policy revision.

continued on next page

Table 5 *continued*

Key Challenge	Description	Likely Impact
POLICY AREA 3: **Financial Engineering**		
Unaddressed Financial Models for Infrastructure Investment	• The policies lack specific financial incentives or partnerships to encourage private sector investment in rapid charging stations.	• Without attractive financial models, private companies may hesitate to invest, leaving gaps in coverage and slowing infrastructure deployment.
Lack of Long-Term Infrastructure Targets	• The policy does not establish specific, measurable targets for the deployment of charging stations by 2030 or beyond. It is only BOI that has projected a need for 12,000 chargers by 2030 and 36,500 chargers by 2035.	• Without clear benchmarks, it becomes challenging to monitor progress, identify gaps, and ensure adequate infrastructure development.
Specific and Separate Targets for Buses and Trucks	• While Thailand's 30@30 policy and related EV strategies focus on promoting ZEVs in passenger vehicles, motorcycles, and club buses and trucks, there is a need to set specific targets for e-buses and e-freight.	• The lack of specific, ambitious targets and corresponding policy measures for these segments may hinder Thailand's ability to meet its decarbonization goals under the NDCs. • For sustainable progress, adopting a more detailed and segmented approach to EV adoption across all vehicle categories is crucial.
Freight Electrification	• No comprehensive framework or significant targets for electrifying heavy freight transport, a major contributor to road transport emissions, are currently evident in Thai policies. • Key challenges, such as the absence of supporting infrastructure like high-capacity charging stations, make freight electrification a low-priority area in existing action plans.	

BEV = battery electric vehicle, BOI = Board of Investment, EV = electric vehicle, NDC = nationally determined contribution, V2G = vehicle-to-grid, ZEV = zero-emission vehicle.
Source: ACGF.

BENCHMARKING THAILAND'S E-MOBILITY POLICIES AGAINST GLOBAL BEST PRACTICES

This assessment compares Thailand's e-mobility policy framework against leading EV-adopting economies to identify strengths, gaps, and opportunities for improvement. The comparative analysis highlights key policy areas, including fiscal incentives, regulatory frameworks, standards, and government support for infrastructure development that have driven e-mobility progress globally and across ASEAN (Table 6).

This section synthesizes these global experiences, summarizing the core strategies and lessons that can inform Thailand's next phase of policy development. Detailed examples and supporting data are provided in Appendix 2.

Table 6: Summary of Key Strategies and Measures from Global and Regional Case Studies

Economy	Key Strategies and Measures	Policy Insights Relevant to Thailand
People's Republic of China (PRC)	The PRC uses a centrally coordinated EV industrial strategy supported by large subsidies; new energy vehicle (including BEVs, PHEVs, and FCEVs) mandates; quota-free license plates; and technical-standard-linked incentives. Extensive battery localization, battery swapping systems, and nationwide fast-charging corridors support rapid mass deployment.	The PRC shows the value of strong central–local coordination and localization policies. Thailand can apply structured industrial support, strengthen battery supply chains, employ city-level measures like registration incentives, and pilot 2W/3W swapping at scale.
Germany	Germany combines generous consumer subsidies (*Umweltbonus*), company car tax reductions, and industrial support policies backed by EU-aligned safety, battery, and recycling rules. It also implements a national charging master plan, strong battery R&D, and grid-integration initiatives.	Germany demonstrates that integrating fiscal incentives with industrial and R&D mandates accelerates manufacturing depth and infrastructure readiness. Thailand can adopt stronger technical standards, invest in R&D, and strengthen OEM–government collaborations.
India	India advances EV adoption through its FAME program (demand subsidies and production-linked incentives), strong focus on 2W/3W, and city-level mandates. PPP-based e-bus programs and widespread swapping for last-mile fleets are now being deployed at scale.	India shows how direct fiscal incentives and urban electrification missions accelerate early adoption. Thailand can adopt similar PPP-based e-bus models, prioritize 2W/3W electrification, and design provincial EV road maps supported by charging and swapping ecosystems.
Indonesia	Indonesia leverages its mineral resources (nickel) to build a battery-manufacturing base, provides incentives for 2W electrification, promotes battery swapping for ride-hailing fleets, and supports EVs through presidential regulations and public procurement.	Indonesia demonstrates how linking EV incentives to domestic resource strength draws investment. Thailand can build mineral-to-battery value chains, promote 2W adoption, and expand operator-led swapping networks to reduce upfront costs.
Japan	Japan maintains a technology-neutral EV policy, supporting BEVs, hybrids, and fuel-cell vehicles. Focus areas include strong safety and charging standards, hydrogen pilots, robust recycling systems, and advanced battery R&D.	Japan shows the value of diversified pathways and resilient end-of-life systems. Thailand can strengthen safety standards, leverage hybrids in the transition period, and explore hydrogen for long-distance and freight applications.
Republic of Korea (ROK)	The ROK deploys EV subsidies, EV-ready building codes, and strong green public procurement. With global battery manufacturers (e.g., LG, Samsung), the ROK links industrial strategy with rapid charging-network expansion and fleet electrification.	The ROK highlights how building regulations and public procurement shape demand. Thailand can incorporate EV-ready building codes, target fleet electrification, and deepen partnerships with Korean OEMs to expand domestic manufacturing capacity.
Norway	Norway follows a comprehensive EV strategy built on strong fiscal incentives (full VAT and purchase-tax exemptions), non-fiscal benefits (toll/parking discounts, bus-lane access), and a clear ICE phase-out by 2025. The country ensures fast-charging availability every 50 kilometers and integrates charging planning with renewable hydroelectricity.	Norway demonstrates that long-term fiscal certainty and consistent regulatory direction accelerate market maturity. Thailand can adopt clear timelines, maintain targeted incentives, and expand national charging corridors to strengthen consumer confidence.
Taipei,China	Taipei,China promotes electrification of 2W fleets through generous subsidies, extensive battery-swapping infrastructure, and city-level regulatory tools such as zero-emission areas. Collaboration with private operators drives rapid uptake in scooters and delivery fleets.	Taipei,China illustrates how aggressive 2W policies can drive large-scale transition quickly. Thailand can scale urban swapping networks, enforce clean-air zones for motorcycles, and incentivize delivery and ride-hailing electrification.

continued on next page

Table 6 *continued*

Economy	Key Strategies and Measures	Policy Insights Relevant to Thailand
United States (US)	The US employs federal tax credits, large-scale charging investments (National EV Infrastructure Program), and state-level ZEV mandates such as those in California. The Inflation Reduction Act links incentives to domestic content and supply chain localization.	The US model highlights how combining incentives with manufacturing subsidies boosts local industry. Thailand can build high-mileage fleet mandates, strengthen BOI localization rules, and create a national intercity fast-charging corridor.
Viet Nam	Viet Nam encourages EV growth via green-growth strategies, excise tax reductions, registration fee waivers, early e-bus pilots, and strong private-sector participation (e.g., VinFast). Cities set EV targets and deploy charging pilots in new developments.	Viet Nam shows that aligning industrial strategy with city-level transport plans accelerates early adoption. Thailand can expand EV bus pilots outside Bangkok, coordinate national and provincial EV programs, and enhance domestic manufacturing through strategic partnerships.

2W = two-wheeler, 3W = three-wheeler, BEV = battery electric vehicle, BOI = Board of Investment, EV = electric vehicle, FAME = Faster Adoption and Manufacturing of Hybrid and E-Vehicles in India, FCEV = fuel cell electric vehicle, ICE = internal combustion engine, OEM = original equipment manufacturer, PHEV = plug-in hybrid electric vehicle, PPP = public–private partnership, ZEV = zero-emission vehicle.
Note: Insights and data from the case studies are as of October 2024.
Source: ACGF.

POLICY INSIGHTS FOR THAILAND'S E-MOBILITY TRANSITION

The global benchmarking highlights that successful e-mobility transitions combine strong fiscal incentives, coordinated infrastructure planning, and long-term industrial strategies. Translating these lessons to the Thai context requires measures that strengthen demand, expand domestic supply capacity, and scale up nationwide charging infrastructure. The following sections outline proposed actions across these three policy drivers: Demand, Supply, and Infrastructure, which together form the foundation of the Thailand E-Mobility Mission 2025–2035.

DEMAND

Key Learnings

1. Expand fiscal measures to address upfront cost differentials in segments such as heavy-duty trucks through direct subsidies, tax exemptions, and low-interest loans, while applying the polluter-pays principle to maintain fiscal neutrality and ensure long-term sustainability.
2. Design targeted affordability programs for rural areas and semi-urban communities to promote equitable access and encourage adoption in underserved vehicle segments.

SUPPLY

Key Learnings

1. Strengthen localization policies and provide targeted incentives to promote domestic EV manufacturing and assembly.
2. Invest in coordinated R&D programs to advance battery technologies and high-value EV components.
3. Foster partnerships with private and international stakeholders to develop a resilient domestic supply chain.

INFRASTRUCTURE

Key Learnings

1. Expand charging networks nationwide, prioritizing both urban and rural areas to ensure reliable and equitable access.
2. Develop policies to integrate solar and wind energy into EV charging systems to enhance grid efficiency and promote renewable-powered charging.
3. Establish and enforce clear standards to ensure interoperability of charging systems across networks and vehicle types.

THAILAND'S CURRENT E-MOBILITY LANDSCAPE

Thailand is moving from early pilots to a scaling phase in its e-mobility transition. It is currently in the barrier lowering phase, focused on expanding early adoption and enabling policies. Figure 13 illustrates this staged progression toward nationwide electrification by 2035.

Figure 13: EV Policy Evolution Road Map

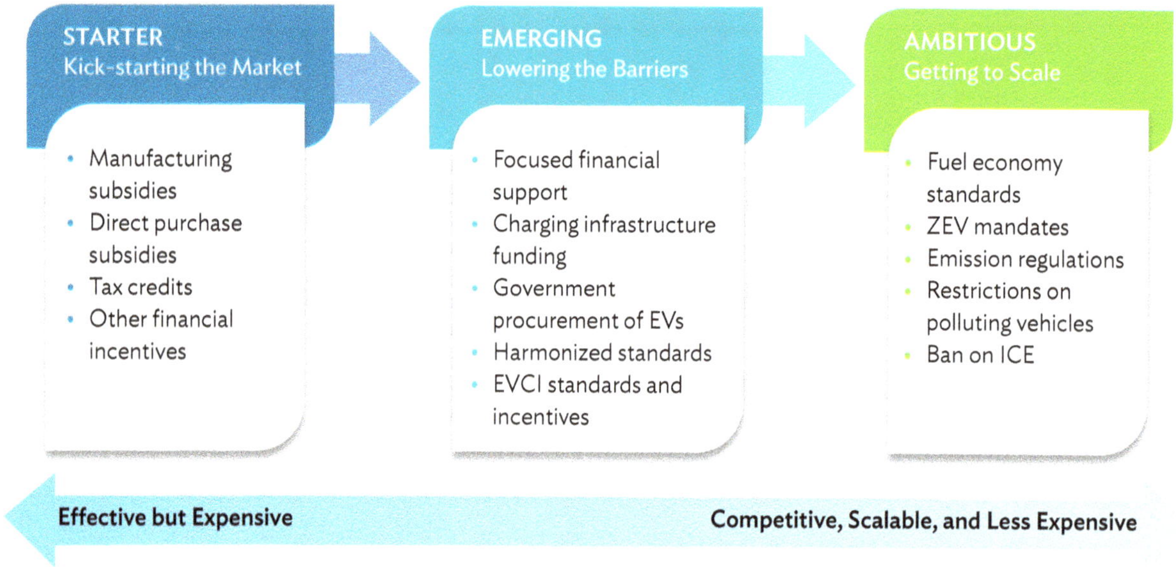

EV = electric vehicle, EVCI = electric vehicle charging infrastructure, ICE = internal combustion engine, ZEV = zero-emission vehicle.
Source: ACGF.

II. REQUIREMENTS FOR SCALING UP INFRASTRUCTURE

Charging infrastructure is a critical enabler of any successful EV ecosystem and a key requirement for Thailand to achieve its ambitious EV targets, including the EV 30@30 policy aiming for 30% ZEV production by 2030. A widespread and user-friendly charging network enhances convenience, reduces range anxiety, and builds consumer confidence in EV adoption, thereby accelerating EV uptake across both personal and commercial segments. For Thailand, where EV penetration is still in its early stages, addressing the gaps in charging infrastructure is critical not only for passenger EVs but also for electrifying public transport and the freight vehicles segment. Without sufficient charging stations, including fast-charging and battery swapping options, the country risks falling short of its EV transition goals, delaying decarbonization in the transport sector and losing its competitive edge as a regional EV manufacturing hub.

This section outlines the e-vehicle charging infrastructure (EVCI) requirements and associated power demand to ensure that Thailand's infrastructure road map aligns with its EV adoption targets and energy system capabilities.

PROJECTIONS FOR SUPPLY EQUIPMENT AND POWER DEMANDS

The global average of EVCI in 2021 stood at 10 EVs per charger and 2.4 kW per EV. The PRC's aggressive expansion of charging infrastructure has since improved global averages to 7 EVs per charger and 3.8 kW per EV, with around 40% of chargers classified as fast charging.[21] As of September 2023, Thailand's ratio of EVs to charging points was higher than the global average, at 18 (Figure 14),[22] indicating that while infrastructure development has progressed, further expansion will be required to meet future EV demand.

Figure 14: Number of EVs per EVSE (as of 2024)

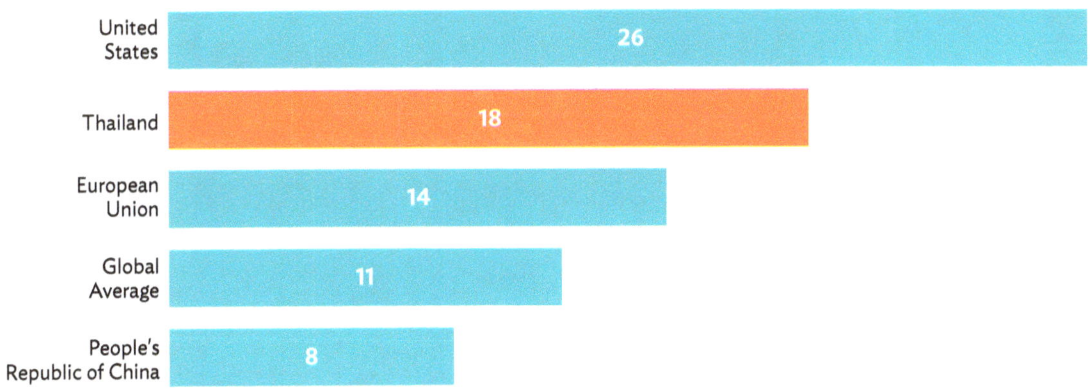

EV = electric vehicle, EVSE = electric vehicle supply equipment.
Source: International Energy Agency.

[21] IEA. Trends in Charging Infrastructure. https://iea.org/reports/global-ev-outlook-2022/trends-in-charging-infrastructure.

[22] IEA. Outlook for electric vehicle charging infrastructure. https://iea.org/reports/global-ev-outlook-2024/outlook-for-electric-vehicle-charging-infrastructure.

SUPPLY EQUIPMENT DEMANDS

To accelerate EV adoption, it is essential to establish a comprehensive and efficient e-vehicle supply equipment (EVSE) network that ensures accessibility, convenience, and consumer confidence. While the 30@30 plan sets an ambitious goal, insufficient charging infrastructure could impede progress, resulting in range anxiety and limited charging options. Proactively expanding EVSE installations is therefore fundamental to facilitating a smooth transition to e-mobility and encouraging broader consumer uptake.

Three deployment scenarios have been considered (Figure 15):

- **As-Is Scenario:** Reflects the current pace of infrastructure development, with approximately 18 ZEVs per charging station (or 24, when including BEVs and PHEVs). This conservative scenario may lead to user challenges and limited charging availability.
- **Global Average Scenario:** Assumes moderate infrastructure expansion, achieving 11 EVs per charging station, aligned with international benchmarks. This balanced approach enhances user convenience and supports steady adoption.
- **Optimistic Scenario:** Envisions significant infrastructure ramp-up to achieve eight EVs per charging station, ensuring widespread accessibility. This ambitious scenario builds user confidence and accelerates EV adoption across the country.

The projected increase in EVSE reflects growing adoption of EVs over the next decade, signaling rising demand for the infrastructure required to support this transition (Table 7).

- **Infrastructure needs:** The demand for EVSE infrastructure will rise sharply, particularly in the Optimistic Scenario. This highlights the need for careful planning and sustained investment in charging stations to match future growth.
- **Long-term planning:** By 2035, EVSE requirements are expected to expand significantly under both the global average and optimistic scenarios. This calls for forward-looking policies and coordinated infrastructure planning.
- **Business opportunities:** Higher EVSE demand presents major opportunities for private sector participation in the development, installation, and operation of charging infrastructure.

Table 7: Projected EVSE Demand from 2025 to 2035

EVSE Requirement to Support EV Projections			
Number of EVSE	**2025**	**2030**	**2035**
As-Is	33,528	62,511	168,878
Global Average	54,864	102,291	276,345
Optimistic	75,438	140,650	379,975

EV = electric vehicle, EVSE = electric vehicle supply equipment.
Source: ACGF.

Figure 15: EVSE Forecast Under Three Scenarios

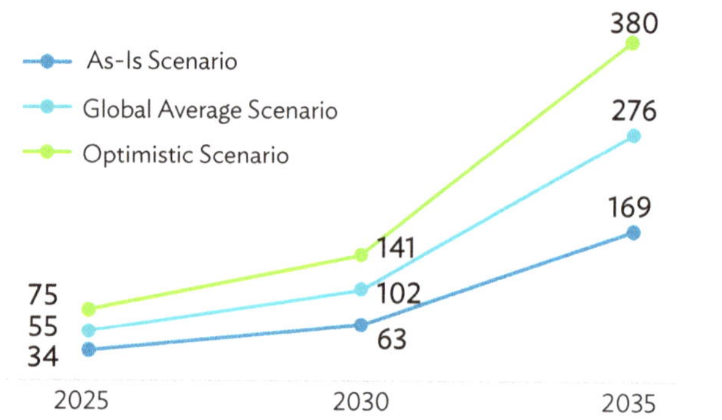

EVSE = electric vehicle supply equipment.
Source: ACGF.

POWER DEMANDS

To estimate power demand for EVs in Thailand, where public data on installed charging capacity and charger-type distribution is limited, reasonable assumptions have been applied to fill these gaps. Average power capacities for each charger type are used as baselines to estimate energy requirements and assess the system's ability to meet future demand. It is further assumed that the average charger capacity increases by 10% year-on-year.

Figure 16: Projected Energy Requirements Under Three Scenarios

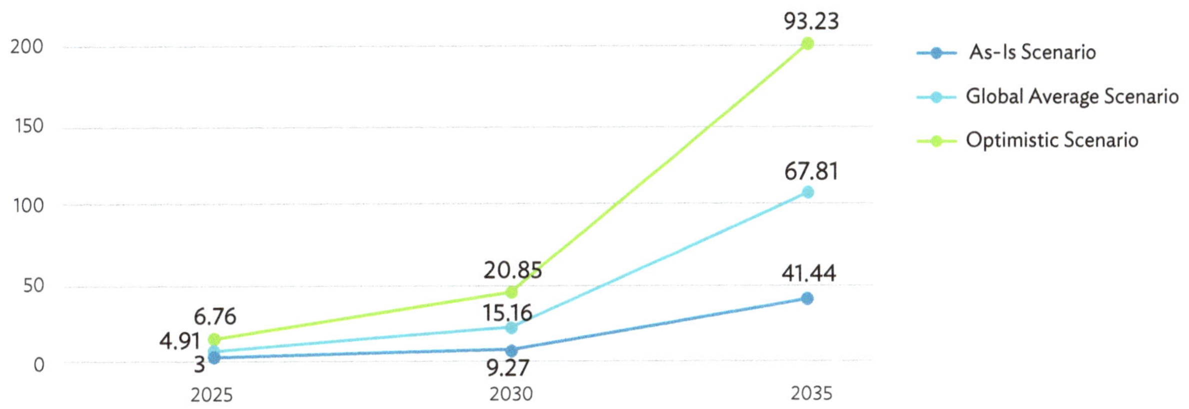

Source: ACGF.

AS-IS SCENARIO

The As-Is Scenario indicates a slow start with substantial capacity expansion occurring only after 2030 (Table 8). This could lead to short-term bottlenecks and hinder EV adoption due to insufficient charging infrastructure.

While this scenario reflects a cautious approach, it risks underserving EV users in the near term and overreliance on a single charging standard. A more balanced and proactive strategy will be critical to meet Thailand's growing EV demand effectively.

Table 8: Aggregated Charging Station Power Capacity for As-Is Scenario (GW)

Type	2025	2030	2035
DC CCS2	2.57	7.73	33.58
DC CHAdeMO	0.15	0.45	1.98
AC Type 2	0.28	1.09	5.87
Total	**3.00**	**9.27**	**41.44**

AC Type 2 = Alternating Current Type 2, DC CCS2 = Direct Current Combined Charging System 2, DC CHAdeMO = Direct Current CHArge de MOve, GW = gigawatt.
Source: ACGF.

GLOBAL AVERAGE SCENARIO

The Global Average Scenario projects a substantial increase in total capacity to 67.81 gigawatts by 2035 (Table 9). It assumes a faster pace of EV adoption, requiring a substantial and accelerated expansion of charging infrastructure.

Given the growth trajectory, Thailand's infrastructure strategy should prioritize the development of DC CCS2 fast-charging stations to meet increasing demand. Concurrently, policy support should continue for AC Type 2 chargers, which remain essential for home and workplace charging.

Table 9: Aggregated Charging Station Power Capacity for Global Average Scenario (GW)

Type	2025	2030	2035
DC CCS2	4.21	12.64	54.95
DC CHAdeMO	0.25	0.74	3.25
AC Type 2	0.46	1.78	9.61
Total	**4.91**	**15.16**	**67.81**

AC Type 2 = Alternating Current Type 2, DC CCS2 = Direct Current Combined Charging System 2, DC CHAdeMO = Direct Current CHArge de MOve, GW = gigawatt.
Source: ACGF.

OPTIMISTIC SCENARIO

This Optimistic Scenario reflects a more proactive approach to expanding the EV charging network, with major investments in both fast-charging technologies and residential-level charging solutions. This is crucial for accelerating EV adoption and achieving Thailand's sustainability and carbon-neutrality goals. It is therefore essential to critically analyze the contributions of different charging standards, the imbalance in their growth rates, and the potential implications for EV adoption in both the short and long term.

This scenario represents a strategic and forward-thinking approach to EV infrastructure development in Thailand. By prioritizing fast-charging networks, particularly DC CCS2, and supporting slower charging options, such as AC Type 2, the government can ensure that the country is well positioned to accommodate the growing demand for EVs (Table 10). While DC CHAdeMO will continue to play a role, focus should remain on scaling up CCS2 infrastructure to align with global standards and future-proof the national charging network. This forward-looking approach will help reduce adoption barriers, accelerate the transition to e-mobility, and position Thailand as a regional leader in green transport.

Table 10: Aggregated Charging Station Power Capacity for Optimistic Scenario (GW)

Type	2025	2030	2035
DC CCS2	5.78	17.38	75.56
DC CHAdeMO	0.34	1.02	4.46
AC Type 2	0.64	2.45	13.31
Total	**6.75**	**20.85**	**93.23**

AC Type 2 = Alternating Current Type 2, DC CCS2 = Direct Current Combined Charging System 2, DC CHAdeMO = Direct Current CHArge de MOve, GW = gigawatt.

KEY FINDINGS

The assessment of Thailand's EV infrastructure highlights both progress and remaining gaps in readiness to support the projected growth in EV adoption. While the focus on fast-charging infrastructure, particularly the DC CCS2 standard, reflects policy ambition, overreliance on a single standard may limit flexibility and inclusiveness. Policy attention must also be extended to battery life-cycle management, including scrapping, collection, safe disposal, and second-life applications. Establishing a framework for responsible end-of-life battery handling will minimize environmental risks and recover valuable materials like cobalt, lithium, and nickel. Promoting second-life battery applications, such as their use in energy storage systems, can extend battery utility and support grid resilience. Furthermore, fast-charging infrastructure for e-buses/ e-trucks should receive targeted financial support, with an estimated initial capital investment of around $50 million.

Despite Thailand's progress under various growth scenarios, its charging infrastructure remains critically underdeveloped to sustain large-scale EV adoption. To meet its targets, Thailand will need to adopt more ambitious policies, establish comprehensive regulatory frameworks, and standardize charging technologies to accelerate infrastructure development and ensure nationwide readiness.

CLEAN ENERGY AND BATTERY SWAPPING

CLEAN ENERGY INTEGRATION

Thailand's energy mix remains heavily reliant on fossil fuels, with renewable energy sources making up 16%, well below the global average of 39%. Despite ongoing efforts to green its energy supply, the country's energy sector remains carbon intensive. Fossil fuels supply 72.1% of electricity generation, led by natural gas (58%), followed by coal (7%).[23] Increasing the share of renewable energy is therefore critical to amplify the environmental benefits of e-mobility.

EVs are inherently more energy efficient, using up to 90% of available energy for traction, compared with only 20%–30% for internal combustion engine (ICE) vehicles. The efficiency makes EVs environmentally advantageous even under the current fossil fuel dominant energy mix. However, the continued reliance on fossil fuels reduces the net GHG benefits of EVs, as both electricity generation and vehicle manufacturing contribute to emissions.

[23] EPPO. 2024. Share of Power Generation by Fuel Type.

Thailand plans to increase its renewable energy share in the medium to long term. Currently, 10% of electricity is derived from biofuels and waste, 5% from wind and solar, and 3% from hydropower.[24] Scaling up these sources is essential to improving the environmental performance of both the EV sector and the broader economy. A key priority should be increasing renewable energy generation to enable a gradual phaseout of coal as the most carbon-intensive fuel source.

Under the Alternative Energy Development Plan 2018-2037, Thailand targets to double its 2021 capacity for biofuels, waste, and wind by 2037, and achieve a fivefold increase in solar capacity.[25] The plan projects renewables energy's share to rise from 18% in 2023 to 51% by 2037, while the reliance on natural gas is projected to decrease from 57% to 41% and coal from 20% to 7%. The remaining 1% of the energy mix will come from nuclear and other emerging energy sources. This presents an opportunity to maximize the e-mobility transition.

Given Thailand's strong solar potential, particularly in the northeastern and southern regions, expanding both utility-scale and rooftop solar installations could play a pivotal role in supporting EV charging demand. This transition will not only enhance the sustainability of the transport sector but also strengthen Thailand's position in achieving its long-term carbon neutrality goals.

BATTERY SWAPPING ECOSYSTEM

Thailand's battery swapping ecosystem has advanced considerably in recent years, driven by both government initiatives and private sector investments. The government's 30@30 target has spurred the development of battery swapping infrastructure to support the growing EV market. Private sector participation has been central to this progress. PTT Group, a state-owned oil and gas company, launched "Swap Go," a battery swapping platform for e-motorcycles. As of 2024, PTT Group's battery swapping subsidiary plans to expand to over 100 service points nationwide, improving accessibility for EV users.[26] Other players in the domestic market include Batt Swap, Electricity Generating Authority of Thailand, ETRAN, Gogoro, H SEM Power Station, Honda PCX Battery Smart, STROM, Winnonie, and ZHI EV Station.

To strengthen this ecosystem, a public–private network has been established to standardize "swappable" batteries for small EVs, notably motorcycles. This initiative brings together agencies such as the Thailand Science Research and Innovation and the Thailand Energy Storage Technology Association to improve battery efficiency and support domestic EV manufacturers.[27] Additionally, companies such as KILATS and STROM Thailand are deploying universal battery swapping platforms to meet the needs of the growing e-motorcycle market,[28] offering flexible and inclusive solutions to overcome barriers to adoption in Southeast Asia.

Despite these advances, challenges remain in standardization and infrastructure expansion. The government, in collaboration with private partners, is working to develop common standards for battery size, connection, and safety to align with international benchmarks. These efforts aim to ensure interoperability, enhance consumer safety, and strengthen investor confidence in Thailand's EV ecosystem.[29]

Recognizing the strategic role of battery swapping in accelerating EV adoption, the Thai government is expected to further incentivize investment in this area. Continued policy and financial support will be essential to establish a robust, accessible, and reliable battery swapping network nationwide. By expanding these services, Thailand can improve convenience for EV users, reduce charging downtime, and advance its broader goals for sustainable and inclusive transport.

---

24 SIPET. Thailand Power Sector Snapshot. https://www.sipet.org/power-sector-snapshot-thailand.aspx.

25 IEA. 2023. Thailand's Clean Electricity Transition. https://shorturl.at/DRxa9.

26 MarkLines. 2023. Thai PTT Group's battery swapping unit set to expand service points to over 100 locations in 2024. https://marklines.com/en.

27 *The Nation*. 2024. Thailand launches network for standardised small EV batteries. 2 August. https://nationthailand.com/business/automobile/40040230.

28 *KILATS*. 2023. KILATS Partners STROM to launch Battery Swap in Thailand. 24 March. https://kilats.com/kilats-partners-strom-to-launch-battery-swap-in-thailand.

29 H. Hamano. 2024. Thailand's Electric Vehicle Market – A Future Powerhouse in Southeast Asia. Kadence International. https://kadence.com/en-us/knowledge/thailands-electric-vehicle-market-a-future-powerhouse-in-southeast-asia.

SWOT ANALYSIS

Thailand's current e-mobility policy framework and the current stage of EV and infrastructure development present both opportunities and challenges. This analysis evaluates the Strengths, Weaknesses, Opportunities, and Threats (SWOT) associated with Thailand's EV policy framework and infrastructure, drawing from the data on vehicle growth, EV adoption trends, and infrastructure development.

Thailand's EV landscape reflects strong government commitment, rapid market growth, and emerging manufacturing capacity, positioning the country as a regional leader in e-mobility. However, critical gaps remain particularly in charging infrastructure coverage, adoption across vehicle segments, integration with clean energy, and the absence of long-term infrastructure targets. Addressing these issues through a coherent and forward-looking policy action plan will be essential to sustaining momentum and achieving national climate and development goals.

Figure 17: SWOT Analysis

EV = electric vehicle; EVSE = electric vehicle supply equipment; SWOT = Strengths, Weaknesses, Opportunities, and Threats; V2G = vehicle-to-grid.

III. ACTION PLAN

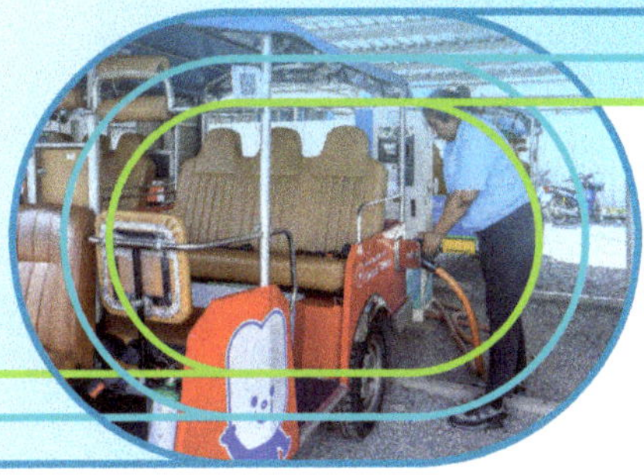

Based on the policy assessment, this study proposes the launch of a Thailand E-Mobility Mission 2025-2035, outlining a comprehensive road map to accelerate the electrification of the transport sector (Figure 18). The mission builds on the existing policy landscape and electrification targets adopted in the EV 3.5 policy. In this way, it aligns with Thailand's climate goals and lays the groundwork for a clean, competitive, and future-ready transport sector that supports the country's targets of net-zero emissions by 2050.

The mission focuses on electrifying public transport and freight systems, expanding nationwide charging infrastructure to ensure accessibility and reliability, and developing a strong domestic EV manufacturing ecosystem that includes batteries and components to enhance local value creation and supply chain resilience. These initiatives should be supported by robust and comprehensive e-mobility policies, alongside national programs for skills development and institutional capacity building to ensure that Thailand's workforce and regulatory systems are equipped to sustain the transition toward a low-carbon transport future.

Thailand's e-mobility transition has progressed through successive policy frameworks—EV 3.0 and EV 3.5—that laid the foundation for manufacturing incentives, vehicle adoption targets, and charging infrastructure development (Table 11). While EV 3.0 initiated fiscal incentives and localization policies, EV 3.5 expanded these through stronger production mandates, consumer subsidies, and technology- neutral standards. The proposed Thailand E-Mobility Mission 2025–2035 builds on these achievements by introducing integrated programs for public transport and freight electrification, national charging infrastructure, domestic battery manufacturing, and large-scale skilling initiatives to align the transport sector with Thailand's carbon-neutrality and net-zero goals.

Figure 18: Proposal for Thailand's E-Mobility Mission 2025–2035

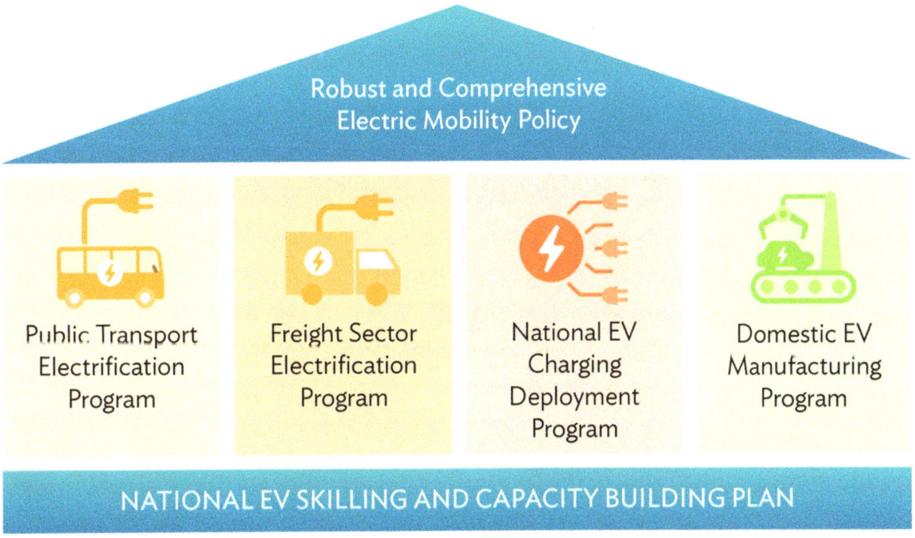

EV = electric vehicle.

Table 11: Evolution of Thailand's E-Mobility Policy Framework: From EV 3.0 and EV 3.5 to the Proposed Thailand E-Mobility Mission 2025–2035

Policy Area	EV 3.0 (2020–2022)	EV 3.5 (2022–2024)	Thailand E-mobility Mission 2025–2035
Strategic Focus	Kick-start EV adoption and local assembly through fiscal incentives.	Scale up domestic manufacturing and expand consumer subsidies.	Integrate public transport, freight, and infrastructure under a unified national mission.
Production Targets	30% ZEV production by 2030 ("30@30").	Reinforced 30@30 with detailed targets for 4-wheelers, 2-wheelers, and buses.	100% electrification of new public transport fleets and 35% electrified freight by 2035.
Fiscal Incentives	Excise-tax reduction and import-duty exemptions.	Direct purchase subsidies (B70,000–B150,000 per EV) plus continued tax relief.	Incentives tied to localization, total-cost-of-ownership, and fleet conversion programs.
Infrastructure	Pilot public charging stations and regulatory guidelines.	Expansion to nationwide fast-charging corridors and standards adoption.	National Charging Deployment Program ensuring universal access and smart-grid integration.
Industry Development	Early localization for batteries and components.	Expanded BOI incentives for battery, motor, and EV parts manufacturing.	Full domestic supply-chain development, R&D hubs, and export capacity for ASEAN markets.
Institutional Mechanism	National EV Policy Committee established.	Inter-agency coordination through EV Board and MOI/BOI.	Dedicated E-mobility Unit under OTP coordinating programs and Green Mobility Fund.
Skills and Capacity	Limited technical training initiatives.	Pilot training with vocational institutes.	Nationwide skilling and certification framework targeting 100,000 EV-related workers per year.

ASEAN = Association of Southeast Asian Nations, BOI = Board of Investment, EV = electric vehicle, MOI = Ministry of Industry, OTP = Office of Transport and Traffic Policy and Planning, R&D = research and development, ZEV = zero-emission vehicle.

Thailand E-Mobility Mission 2025-2035

VISION

"To position Thailand as a self-reliant and globally recognized leader in sustainable e-mobility, delivering cleaner air, healthier communities, and affordable transportation solutions through local innovation and an inclusive EV ecosystem."

E-ferry, on Chao Phraya river, at the Tha Chang Pier, near the Grand Palace (photo by ADB).

POLICY DRIVER CHECKLIST

For e-mobility, these are the guiding questions to ask before determining policy measures, and they informed all proposals under this mission.

DEMAND

Demand-side measures play a crucial role in promoting e-mobility in Thailand by encouraging consumers to adopt EVs over traditional ICE vehicles. These policies must tackle both affordability and awareness to build confidence in EV ownership.

- ☐ How will the policy incentivize consumers to choose EVs over traditional ICE vehicles?
- ☐ What financial incentives, such as subsidies, tax credits, or rebates, will make EVs more affordable and competitive with conventional vehicles?
- ☐ How will the policy address the higher upfront cost of EVs and promote awareness of the long-term savings associated with EV ownership, including lower fuel and maintenance costs?
- ☐ How will the policy raise awareness among consumers about the environmental, health, and energy security benefits of EVs?
- ☐ How will the policy leverage partnerships with automakers, dealerships, utilities, and environmental organizations to educate consumers and facilitate the transition to e-mobility?

SUPPLY

Supply-side measures ensure that EVs and their components are readily available, affordable, and tailored to the local market. Strong coordination among government, industry, and research institutions is essential to strengthen Thailand's manufacturing competitiveness.

- ☐ What measures will support the transition of auto manufacturers to EV production in line with Thailand's industrial strategy?
- ☐ How will the policy incentivize investment in the production and sale of EVs, including passenger cars, buses, trucks, and 2-wheelers?
- ☐ What regulatory measures are required to create a favorable environment for EV manufacturing, sales, and servicing, including standards, certification processes, and consumer protection?
- ☐ How will the policy foster collaboration among industry stakeholders, research institutions, and government agencies to drive innovation and technological advancement, and workforce skilling in the e-mobility sector?
- ☐ What incentives will encourage investment in local manufacturing capabilities for EV components such as batteries, e-motors, and charging equipment to strengthen supply chain resilience?

INFRASTRUCTURE

A robust charging network is the foundation of Thailand's e-mobility transition. Policies must ensure that infrastructure deployment keeps pace with EV adoption and supports seamless access across the country.

- ☐ How will the policy ensure widespread coverage and accessibility of charging infrastructure across urban, suburban, and rural areas?
- ☐ What measures will prioritize the deployment of charging stations along major transport corridors and at key destinations such as shopping centers, workplaces, and public facilities?
- ☐ How will the policy promote the rollout of fast-charging infrastructure for private vehicles, public transport, and freight fleets to minimize charging time and reduce range?
- ☐ How will the policy ensure interoperability and standardization of EV charging infrastructure to guarantee compatibility and ease of use across different charging networks and platforms?
- ☐ How will the policy support open-source platforms and secure data-sharing protocols to encourage collaboration and innovation while protecting consumer privacy and system security?

50 PROPOSED MEASURES

Policy drivers are critical as they form the foundation for creating effective, targeted, and impactful strategies. They help align policy actions with national priorities, stakeholder needs, and global trends, ensuring a coherent and sustainable approach to electrifying the transport sector (Figure 19).

This section presents a proposed set of 50 policy measures that support and operationalize the Thailand E-Mobility Mission 2025–2035 (Table 12). These measures are designed to address the country's current challenges and leverage emerging opportunities, drawing on global and regional best practices as well as existing national policy frameworks and sustainability targets.

Some of these measures are already included in Thailand's current policy landscape, others are partially addressed, and several represent new interventions that could fill existing policy gaps. Collectively, they form a coherent road map to accelerate the transition to clean, efficient, and inclusive mobility solutions in Thailand.

Figure 19: Proposed Policy Framework

DEMAND SIDE

1. Market Development and Consumer Incentives
2. Consumer Awareness and Communication
3. Demand Assessment and Aggregation

SUPPLY SIDE

4. Tax Incentives
5. Vehicle Emission and Clean-Fuel Standards
6. Targets and Mandates
7. Research Development and Capacity Building

INFRASTRUCTURE SIDE

8. User-Centric Charging Infrastructure
9. Codes and Standards
10. Funding Resources and Institutional Setup

Table 12: Proposed Policy Measures

Policy Area	Policy Measure
	POLICY DRIVER: DEMAND
Market Development and Consumer Incentives	1. Adopt a vehicle-based electrification approach suited to Thailand's emerging e-mobility market, with particular focus on modes requiring accelerated transition. While car segment electrification is progressing, policy measures should initially prioritize electric 2-/3-wheelers (including e-bikes), e-buses for public and school transport, intraurban freight EVs and shared EVs such as ride-hailing and delivery fleets. Promote EV rentals in major tourist hubs such as Phuket and Pattaya to encourage sustainable travel options. In Phase 2, extend efforts to include e-rail systems, e-water transport, and interurban green freight solutions. 2. Implement fleet electrification programs to transition priority vehicle categories across public sector fleets, including the phased conversion of government vehicles to electric power. Establish minimum local content requirements for government EV procurement to stimulate demand and strengthen Thai manufacturing. 3. Provide financial incentives, such as interest subvention, purchase rebates, or tax credits, to reduce the up-front cost of EV ownership. This would provide direct financial relief to consumers and make EVs more affordable than traditional ICE vehicles. Conduct TCO analysis by vehicle type to identify viability gaps and tailor incentive levels accordingly. 4. Offer tax- and fee-based incentives, including reduced or waived vehicle registration fees and green tax credits for EV purchases, to make EV ownership more affordable and competitive with conventional vehicles. 5. Provide additional green tax credits to consumers who purchase EVs to further stimulate demand. By incentivizing consumer adoption through fiscal incentives, this measure supports both market expansion and domestic industry growth. 6. Develop a national incentive scheme for businesses and fleet operators to support the transition to EVs, including subsidies or preferential financing for purchasing EVs. This would help accelerate the electrification of commercial fleets and public transport systems. 7. Provide incentives for purchasing used EVs, coupled with strict battery testing and residual life requirements to prevent the import of low-quality imports or unsafe vehicles into Thailand. 8. Introduce incentives for retrofitting existing ICE vehicles into EVs, including financial and regulatory support to develop a domestic retrofit industry. 9. Designate clean vehicles or EV-only zones in Bangkok and other major urban areas as pilots to reduce air pollution, improve visibility of EVs, and encourage adoption.
Consumer Awareness and Communications	10. Launch a nationwide awareness campaign to promote EV adoption highlighting environmental and economic benefits and available incentives, and addressing concerns about cost, maintenance, and charging. The campaign should target both urban and rural populations through multiple media platforms and community-based initiatives. 11. Develop a centralized national EV portal consolidating information on incentives, regulations, charging locations, and technical guidelines. The portal should serve as a one-stop platform for consumers, businesses, and government agencies to access reliable and updated resources on e-mobility. 12. Institutionalize hosting an annual National Clean Transport Summit to foster partnerships, showcase technological advancements, and assess policy progress and effectiveness.
Demand Assessment and Aggregation	13. Coordinate across government procurement agencies to assess and aggregate EV demand through a centralized procurement mechanism. Aggregating demand can lower costs, standardize specifications, and stimulate market growth across the e-mobility ecosystem. 14. Establish a nodal procurement agency to manage EV procurement for government departments, public sector units, transport authorities, and other government entities, enabling economies of scale and consistent implementation of fleet electrification goals.

continued on next page

Table 11 *continued*

Policy Area	Policy Measure
	**POLICY DRIVER:** SUPPLY
Tax Incentives	15. Provide supply-side tax incentives to encourage manufacturers, assemblers, suppliers, and other industry stakeholders to invest in EV production and deployment, particularly BEVs. Incentive mechanisms may include: a. **Investment tax credits**: For manufacturers and suppliers of EVs and components such as batteries, e-motors, and charging infrastructure to offset capital investment costs for new technologies, expanded production capacity, or upgraded manufacturing facilities. b. **Production tax credits**: For manufacturers based on EV output or manufacturing capacity to reduce production costs and enhance competitiveness. c. **R&D tax credits**: For research and development (R&D) in EV technology, battery innovation, and charging infrastructure to stimulate innovation and cost reductions. d. **Accelerated depreciation**: Allow accelerated depreciation for EV manufacturing assets and equipment to improve cash-flow benefits and reduce capital costs. e. **Customs and import duties exemptions**: Waive or reduce customs duties and import tariffs on critical EV parts and materials to lower production costs and support local assembly. 16. Simplify and expedite regulatory approval processes for new EV models, manufacturing facilities, and charging infrastructure to reduce administrative bottlenecks and support faster market entry.
Vehicle Emissions and Clean Fuel Standards	17. Introduce stronger vehicle emissions and clean fuels standards to create a supportive regulatory environment for sustainable transport. This should address emissions from the existing vehicle fleet while promoting the transition to cleaner fuels and low-emission vehicles. 18. Appoint an expert committee to review and update Thailand's existing vehicle and clean fuel standards, including: a. **Stringent vehicle emissions standards**: Enforce progressively tighter limits on pollutants such as nitrogen oxides, particulate matter, carbon monoxide, and hydrocarbons, and require onboard emissions control systems such as catalytic converters and particulate filters. b. **Phaseout of conventional vehicles**: Establish timelines for ending the sale of new ICE vehicles, ensuring a phased transition toward electric or ZEVs. c. **Mandates for clean and efficient fuel use**: Require the use of cleaner fuels such as low-sulfur gasoline and diesel, biofuels, hydrogen, or synthetic fuels. Consider adopting corporate average fuel efficiency standards to reduce life-cycle emissions. d. **Incentives for clean fuel infrastructure**: Provide fiscal or regulatory incentives for developing hydrogen refueling, biofuel blending, and other clean-fuel facilities. e. **Vehicle inspection and maintenance programs**: Strengthen vehicle inspections and maintenance systems to ensure compliance with emissions standards and proper operation of control systems. f. **Collaboration with industry stakeholders**: Work with automakers, fuel suppliers, industry associations, and other stakeholders to develop, implement, and align clean-fuel policies and emissions standards with market readiness and technical feasibility.

continued on next page

Table 11 *continued*

Policy Area	Policy Measure
Targets and Mandates	19. Introduce a ZEV mandate to accelerate the supply of affordable EVs in Thailand. This could include: a. **ZEV sales targets**: Establish phased targets requiring automakers to achieve a growing share of ZEV sales, including BEVs, PHEVs, and FCVs, over time. b. **Compliance mechanisms**: Define penalties, tradable credits, or alternative compliance options to ensure manufacturers meet ZEV targets. c. **Carbon credit mechanism**: Introduce carbon credit schemes that reward companies and individuals for EV use. d. **Credit trading program**: Enable automakers to trade ZEV credits to meet their compliance obligations and incentivize innovation and investment in EV technology. e. **Credit multipliers**: Offer credit multipliers for advanced ZEV types, such as hydrogen fuel cell or long-range vehicles, to spur innovation. f. **ZEV infrastructure requirements**: Require automakers to invest in ZEV infrastructure, such as charging stations, as part of their compliance obligations. g. **Flexibility mechanisms**: Provide flexibility mechanisms, such as banking and borrowing credits or carrying over credits from previous compliance periods, to ease the transition and accommodate market fluctuations. h. **Monitoring and reporting requirements**: Mandate transparent reporting of automaker progress toward ZEV targets. 20. Set up an expert group to design and periodically review the mechanism for implementing a ZEV mandate, including target setting, compliance monitoring, and stakeholder coordination.
R&D and Capacity Building	21. Provide government funding and grants to Thai universities and research institutions for R&D on EVs, battery technology, charging infrastructure, and smart mobility solutions to drive innovation and technological advancements. 22. Offer tax incentives, such as tax credits or deductions, for businesses investing in REV and clean transport innovation, encouraging private sector-led research and development. 23. Establish a national e-mobility living lab through PPPs as a testbed for pilot projects and industry collaboration. The lab should facilitate data sharing, joint research, and commercialization of new EV technologies and solutions. 24. Set up centers of excellence or innovation hubs on e-mobility in leading Thai universities to foster collaboration among academia, industry, and government, supporting technology transfer and applied and interdisciplinary research. 25. Develop industry standards and certification programs for EV technologies, charging infrastructure, and related components to ensure interoperability, safety, and quality assurance. 26. Establish incubators, accelerators, or innovation centers, including a dedicated special economic zone for e-mobility startups, to support entrepreneurship and attract global partnerships focused on EV and fuel cell innovation. 27. Implement capacity-building programs, such as training, workshops, and education initiatives, to upskill and reskill workers for jobs in the growing e-mobility sector. Partner with international organizations and development finance institutions to scale training and knowledge exchange. 28. Mandate data sharing on EV usage patterns, charging behavior, and infrastructure demand to inform strategic planning, policy, and investment decisions while ensuring data privacy and interoperability. 29. Engage in international collaboration and knowledge-sharing initiatives with other countries and global organizations to exchange best practices, leverage R&D funding, and access cutting-edge expertise in EV technologies and policy design.

continued on next page

Table 11 *continued*

Policy Area	Policy Measure
	**POLICY DRIVER:** INFRASTRUCTURE
User-Centric Charging Infrastructure	30. Develop a National EV Charging Master Plan setting clear targets for deploying fast and slow EV chargers across urban, suburban, and rural areas to ensure reliable nationwide coverage and accessibility. 31. Encourage PPPs to leverage resources, expertise, and investment from both government and private sector stakeholders to accelerate the deployment of fast-charging infrastructure and address financing challenges. 32. Streamline regulatory processes and permitting requirements for installing EV charging stations to reduce administrative burdens, expedite deployment, and lower costs for infrastructure developers and operators. 33. Support utility investments in EV charging and grid integration by offering incentives, tariff structures, and demand-response programs to manage electricity demand and ensure grid reliability. 34. Provide tax incentives or grants for installing home and public charging stations to improve accessibility, reduce range anxiety, and encourage early adoption. 35. Offer accelerated depreciation or investment tax credits for businesses investing in charging infrastructure to expand the charging network and attract private capital. 36. Develop energy storage systems to support grid stability, efficient charging infrastructure, and renewable energy integration. 37. Facilitate digital platforms that map charging stations, display real-time availability, and support trip planning and payment interoperability. 38. Develop battery swapping infrastructure and related incentives, focusing on high use segments such as freight transport and delivery fleets. 39. Introduce green logistics corridors powered by EVs to decarbonize supply chains and demonstrate large-scale zero-emission freight solutions.
Codes and Standards	40. Harmonize national codes and standards for EV infrastructure, charging equipment, and vehicle-to-X (V2G, V2V, V2H) technologies to ensure consistency, interoperability, and compatibility across regions and platforms. 41. Establish interoperability standards for EV charging infrastructure to enable seamless connectivity and usability across multiple charging providers and vehicle types. 42. Implement certification and compliance requirements for EVs, charging equipment, and related infrastructure to ensure product safety, reliability, and quality assurance. 43. Update building codes and regulations to require EV-ready provisions in new residential, commercial, and public buildings, including electrical wiring, parking, and safety measures. 44. Establish battery recycling policies and facilities to manage end-of-life batteries sustainably and introduce a digital "battery passport" to track origin, use, and recycling. 45. Establish data security and privacy standards for EV charging networks and smart charging systems to protect consumer data, ensure confidentiality, and prevent unauthorized access or misuse of personal information. 46. Establish mechanisms for periodic review and update of codes and standards to reflect technological advancements, safety lessons, and international best practice.

continued on next page

Table 11 *continued*

Policy Area	Policy Measure
Funding, Resources, and Institutional Structure	47. Establish a robust institutional framework to accelerate the adoption of e-mobility, which could include a dedicated "E-Mobility Unit" within OTP to coordinate nationwide EV initiatives. The unit would serve as a technical arm of the National EV Board, overseeing policy formulation, financial mechanisms, and regulatory implementation to address barriers in scaling e-mobility. 48. Create a green mobility fund to finance EV projects, research initiatives, and infrastructure development. The fund could be capitalized through public contributions, private investments, or revenues from EV sales and charging fees, with proceeds reinvested to sustain long-term e-mobility development. 49. Implement carbon pricing mechanisms, such as carbon taxes or emissions trading systems, and channel a portion of revenues to fund EV incentives, infrastructure projects, and climate-related investments. This would internalize the social and environmental costs of emissions and encourage clean transport adoption. 50. Encourage PPPs to leverage resources, expertise, and investment from both government and private sector stakeholders to support EV deployment and infrastructure development. PPP frameworks should facilitate collaboration, share risks and rewards, and accelerate progress toward shared goals in the e-mobility sector.

BEV = battery electric vehicle, EV = electric vehicle, FCV = fuel cell vehicle, ICE = internal combustion engine, PHEV = plug-in hybrid electric vehicle, OTP = Office of Transport and Traffic Policy and Planning, PPP = public–private partnership, TCO = total cost of ownership, V2G = vehicle-to-grid, V2H = vehicle-to-home, V2V = vehicle-to-vehicle, ZEV = zero-emission vehicle.

FLAGSHIP PROGRAMS

The proposed mission is designed to accelerate the transition from fragmented e-mobility initiatives toward a unified approach that integrates public transport modernization, freight decarbonization, infrastructure development, and domestic manufacturing. By aligning stakeholders across government, industry, and finance, the mission seeks to create enabling conditions for a scaled, equitable, and resilient e-mobility ecosystem.

The following section outlines the five flagship programs proposed under the mission.

PUBLIC TRANSPORT ELECTRIFICATION

This program aims to decarbonize Thailand's urban and intercity transit systems by replacing traditional ICE vehicles with electric alternatives. Key targets include the deployment of 3,390 e-buses in Bangkok by 2030, the establishment of an electric bus rapid transit, or BRT, in Phuket, and the rollout of e-buses on intercity routes supported by green terminal infrastructure. Over the next decade, Bangkok will gradually electrify its entire fleet to e-buses, while other major cities will expand BRT systems and e-bus operations.

The program also promotes the electrification of water and rail transport. In Bangkok, e-boats already operate across key waterways, enhancing connectivity while reducing air and noise pollution. The plan further includes the introduction of 50 e-locomotives for urban and intercity rail routes to deliver low-emission, energy-efficient operations. Comprehensive charging infrastructure, including fast chargers and battery swapping stations, will be deployed to support these initiatives and ensure high fleet uptime and operational efficiency.

PARTNERS AND STAKEHOLDERS

MOF: Payment security mechanisms and financing support.

ERC: Tariff structures and grid reliability.

OTP: Lead agency for program design and implementation.

BMTA and TCL: Fleet procurement and operations.

Provincial Transit Authorities: Regional deployment.

Private Operators: Bus supply, operation, and maintenance.

TIMELINE

2025–2027	2028–2032	2033–2035
Electrification of 25% of fleet in Bangkok; pilot in 5 other cities.	Scale up to regional/intercity services; 40%–50% public transport electrified.	Full electrification of public bus fleets in major cities.

FREIGHT SECTOR ELECTRIFICATION

This program targets achieving a 35% share of freight EVs by 2035, focusing on medium- and heavy-duty trucks and urban delivery vehicles. The goal is to decarbonize Thailand's logistics and freight sectors through a combination of fiscal incentives, infrastructure investment, and technology innovation. Key elements include battery swapping stations to minimize vehicle downtime, green logistics hubs equipped with charging infrastructure, and tax reductions and grants to support fleet operators transitioning to electric solutions.
The program emphasizes PPPs to expand charging networks, smart fleet management systems to enhance operational efficiency, and integration of advanced digital technologies to optimize logistics operations. By addressing both operational efficiency and environmental impact, this initiative aims to transform Thailand's freight and logistics industry into a sustainable, competitive, and low-emission model, contributing directly to the country's carbon neutrality and net-zero commitments.

PARTNERS AND STAKEHOLDERS

OTP: Lead policy and road map coordination.

Department of Land Transport: Regulatory oversight of freight vehicles.

Federation of Thai Industries and EVAT: Industry engagement and standards.

BMTA and TCL: Infrastructure and fleet conversion.

Logistics Providers and Industrial Park Operators: Incentivization and manufacturing linkages

TIMELINE

2025–2026	2027–2031	2032–2035
Urban logistics pilots; grants for charging hubs.	Fast-charging corridors on highways; incentives for long-haul fleets.	Zero-emission logistics zones in industrial areas.

NATIONAL ELECTRIC VEHICLE CHARGING DEPLOYMENT

This program aims to establish a nationwide network of fast-charging stations for e-cars, complemented by battery swapping facilities and home-charging solutions that align with global best practices. The goal is to address range anxiety and enable widespread EV adoption by ensuring reliable coverage across urban, semi-urban, and intercity routes. The program emphasizes smart grid integration and interoperability standards to optimize energy use and guarantee compatibility across different EV models and charging platforms. PPPs play a key role, encouraging investments from energy providers, automakers, and tech firms to scale infrastructure deployment. Financial incentives, including tax breaks, grants, and cofinancing mechanisms, will accelerate private participation and ensure cost-effective expansion of Thailand's charging ecosystem.

PARTNERS AND STAKEHOLDERS

ERC: Grid and charging policy.

EPPO and Ministry of Energy (MOE): Clean energy integration.

Thai Industrial Standards Institute and DEDE: Standards and safety certifications.

OTP: Infrastructure planning, location intelligence.

Private Investors: Deployment, operation.

TIMELINE

2025–2027	2028–2032	2033–2035
National master plan rollout; 20,000 charging points.	Coverage expansion to semi-urban and rural regions.	Universal access; integration with smart grid and battery swapping.

DOMESTIC ELECTRIC VEHICLE MANUFACTURING

Thailand aims to establish itself as a self-reliant EV production hub in Southeast Asia, targeting the ability to meet 100% of domestic demand for e-buses and 2- and 3-wheelers by 2035. This program will incentivize local production of key components, such as batteries and traction motors, to strengthen the domestic supply chain and reduce import dependence. The program will provide robust incentives to manufacturers, including corporate income tax exemptions, import duty reductions for machinery and raw materials, and grants for R&D initiatives focused on EV technologies. It also fosters strategic partnerships between global automakers and Thai firms to facilitate technology transfer, joint ventures, and upskilling of the local workforce.

In addition to domestic market goals, the program positions Thailand as a regional EV export hub, capable of producing competitive EVs and components for ASEAN markets. Comparable targets can be set for other vehicle categories, in consultation with industry stakeholders and in line with evolving demand and market readiness.

PARTNERS AND STAKEHOLDERS

BOI and Ministry of Industry: Investment incentives and industrial policy.

NSTDA: R&D and innovation support.

EV Manufacturers and OEMs: Implementation and supply chain development.

EVAT: Industry coordination and standards.

Ministry of Higher Education, Science, Research and Innovation: Research grants and academic collaboration.

TIMELINE

2025–2026	2027–2030	2031–2035
Incentives and localization targets announced.	30% domestic content in key EV segments.	Thailand as regional export hub for EVs and components.

NATIONAL ELECTRIC VEHICLE SKILLING AND CAPACITY BUILDING

This program prepares a skilled workforce capable of supporting Thailand's growing EV ecosystem, covering manufacturing, infrastructure development, maintenance, and policy implementation. It seeks to address current skills gaps and create a talent pool equipped with competencies required across the EV value chain. The program emphasizes hands-on training, cutting-edge curricula, and certification programs aligned with domestic and global EV industry standards.

In manufacturing, training will focus on assembly line operations for e-cars, e-motorcycles, e-buses, and e-trucks, including the production and management of advanced battery systems. Participants will also gain skills in handling powertrain components such as motors, inverters, and thermal management systems, and in battery assembly, maintenance, recycling, and disposal to ensure sustainable end-of-life management. Training will extend to charging infrastructure development, covering installation, maintenance, smart grid integration, and cybersecurity protocols for connected systems. Modules may also include software development, telematics, and data analytics for EV fleet management and infrastructure planning.

PARTNERS AND STAKEHOLDERS

OTP: National skilling framework coordination.

Office of the Vocational Education Commission and Department of Skill Development: Curriculum delivery.

Ministry of Higher Education, Science, Research and Innovation and NSTDA: Advanced training and certifications.

Private EV Sector: Industry-aligned training partnerships.

Development Partners: Technical assistance and capacity building.

TIMELINE

2025–2026	2027–2031	2032–2035
National skilling strategy, training facility upgrades.	Annual training of 50,000 skilled workers in EV-related fields.	Scale up to 100,000/year; specialized programs in AI, battery recycling, and EV software.

The program targets a wide range of participants, including industry professionals transitioning from conventional automotive roles, students and engineers entering the workforce, policymakers involved in EV program design, and private sector entrepreneurs and researchers driving innovation.

Delivery will be ensured through partnerships with global think tanks, multilateral organizations, global automakers, technology providers, and academic institutions. Specialized training centers equipped with simulation systems will be established in key industrial hubs, supported by digital learning platforms for nationwide access. A national certification framework aligned with international standards will ensure enhanced employability in both domestic and global EV markets. Financial incentives, including scholarships and grants, will encourage participation, particularly among underserved communities, promoting equity and inclusivity across the workforce transition.

PHASING PLAN

Implementation of the e-mobility mission should follow a phased approach that builds a strong foundation, scales successful programs, and ensures long-term sustainability. The plan is divided into three key phases—Foundation Building (2025–2027), Expansion and Scaling (2028–2032), and Maturity and Sustainability (2033–2035)—each with distinct priorities and milestones.

PHASE 1: FOUNDATION BUILDING (2025–2027)

The initial phase will focus on creating conditions for rapid adoption through fiscal and non-fiscal incentives, including purchase subsidies for EV buyers, tax exemptions for manufacturers, and support for domestic EV component production.

- **Public transport:** Begin e-bus expansion in Bangkok under BMTA and TCL, integrating pilot fleets into existing transport routes.
- **Freight sector:** Electrify key urban logistics routes, supported by grants for charging hubs and early fleet transitions.
- **Infrastructure:** Establish fast-charging corridors in urban centers along key highways.
- **Manufacturing:** Provide financial support to domestic producers of batteries and key components to enhance localization.
- **Skilling:** Launch vocational and university-level training programs to develop the first generation of EV technicians and engineers.

PHASE 2: EXPANSION AND SCALING (2028–2032)

This phase will focus on mainstreaming electrification across sectors and regions.

- Strengthen emission norms and develop EV recycling infrastructure for sustainable waste management.
- Expand e-bus deployment to regional cities and intercity routes, targeting 40%–50% electrification of public transport systems by 2032.
- Extend freight electrification to long-haul logistics, supported by an expanded network of charging hubs in industrial areas.
- Scale up charging infrastructure to cover semi-urban and rural areas, ensuring equitable access.
- Achieve 30% domestic localization in EV and component manufacturing, reinforcing Thailand's role as regional production hub.
- Train at least 50,000 individuals annually in EV production, maintenance, and infrastructure development.

PHASE 3: MATURITY AND SUSTAINABILITY (2033–2035)

The final phase will aim for full electrification of public transport systems and zero-emission freight fleets along all major routes.

- Ensure universal access to EV charging infrastructure integrated with smart-grid technologies for optimized operations.

- Strengthen domestic EV manufacturing to compete globally, establishing Thailand as the leading EV production hub in the ASEAN region.
- Establish advanced training facilities and research centers focused on specialized expertise in battery recycling, software development, and smart-charging solutions.
- Scale up skilling programs to train 100,000 skilled professionals annually, ensuring a sustainable pipeline of EV talent.

This phased approach will ensure that Thailand's EV transition remains adaptive, inclusive, and aligned with national climate commitments and supportive of sustainable economic growth.

PARTNERS AND STAKEHOLDERS

MOF and BOI: Incentive and financing mechanisms.

Ministry of Industry and Office of Industrial Economics: Industry support, standards development.

EV Board: Policy oversight and inter-agency coordination.

OTP: Overall coordination, strategic road map development, monitoring.

Energy Policy and Planning Office (EPPO): EV registration, safety compliance.

Department of Land Transport: Charging infrastructure integration with power systems.

EVAT and Private Sector: Industry implementation and advocacy.

TIMELINE

2025–2027	2028–2032	2033–2035
Legal and regulatory review; inter-agency MoUs; launch of incentive schemes.	Institutionalization of mandates; expansion of demand-side and infrastructure-side programs.	Scaling national coverage and deepening localization efforts.

FINANCING AND THE WAY FORWARD

To ensure successful implementation, the action plan proposes the establishment of a dedicated fund to pool, allocate, and manage resources effectively for clean transport initiatives. It also calls for a payment security mechanism and a robust monitoring and evaluation (M&E) system to ensure accountability and transparency. Stakeholder engagement and capacity building will be central, supported by an adaptive management framework that allows programs to evolve with changing needs. A dedicated unit within OTP will oversee electrification efforts, ensuring alignment with Thailand's national climate goals.

The proposed **Green Mobility Fund** would address the financing bottlenecks and enable timely implementation of e-mobility initiatives. By pooling diverse funding sources and employing a strong governance framework, the fund will play a catalytic role in advancing Thailand's NDC commitments and long-term climate resilience. While detailed design will require further consultation, the preliminary structure could include the following elements:

- Pool resources from public budgets, international climate finance, private sector investments, and green bonds.
- Serve as a centralized repository for sustainable transport financing.
- De-risk private sector participation through blended finance mechanisms, guarantees, and co-financing.
- Prioritize allocation to high-impact projects aligned with Thailand's NDC targets and e-mobility road map.
- Implement transparent systems for fund use and emissions tracking.
- Capacity-building support to local governments, transport operators, and private entities in project design and execution.

The fund could be anchored within a national coordinating entity, working in collaboration with the Ministry of Finance (MOF), the National Economic and Social Development Council, and relevant line ministries. A multistakeholder governing board comprising representatives from government, development partners, financial institutions, and private sector stakeholders would oversee fund governance, strategic alignment, and transparency.

To ensure efficiency, the fund may operate through dedicated financing windows targeting electric public transport, EV charging infrastructure, low-emission freight logistics, and subnational capacity building. This structure would streamline allocation, simplify project appraisal, and ensure that resources are directed toward high-impact areas aligned with Thailand's e-mobility road map.

To further accelerate implementation, a payment security mechanism should be established as a risk mitigation tool within the facility to enhance private sector confidence. This mechanism would ensure financial security for private operators investing in e-bus fleets, reducing perceived risks and addressing barriers to entry. By guaranteeing payments and mitigating operational risks, it would attract private investment and expedite the electrification of urban transport systems such as in Bangkok.

The fund's governance framework should also embed an inclusive and transparent stakeholder engagement process to facilitate communication, outreach, and technical support. This would help subnational authorities, transport operators, and private entities access and use funding effectively. A national program framework should prioritize eligible projects, standardize appraisal criteria, and align financing decisions with national and sector decarbonization goals. Over time, this institutional and participatory setup would enable the fund to evolve into a scalable and credible platform for mobilizing climate-aligned investments in the transport sector for Thailand.

KEY FEATURES

The action plan adopts an integrated and forward-looking approach to accelerate Thailand's e-mobility transition. Its key features include:

- **Integrated strategies:** The plan combines demand-, supply-, and infrastructure-side measures to create a cohesive ecosystem for e-mobility growth. The strategies complement Thailand's broader EV 3.5 plan and align with specific electrification initiatives, ensuring consistency and reinforcing national targets.
- **Institutional coordination and capacity development:** Cross-cutting measures are designed to strengthen institutional capacity, streamline coordination among government agencies and stakeholders, and address technical and financial barriers. This will ensure policy coherence and effective implementation across sectors.
- **Innovative financing mechanism:** A Green Mobility Fund is proposed as a dedicated financial mechanism to attract and mobilize investments for clean transport projects. This fund will serve as a catalytic vehicle, leveraging public, private, and international climate finance sources to accelerate e-mobility investments.
- **Robust M&E framework:** The road map recommends establishing a comprehensive M&E system with key performance indicators to systematically track progress, ensure accountability, and evaluate the effectiveness of implemented actions. This framework will enable continuous improvement and adaptive policymaking.

NEXT STEPS

Successful implementation of the e-mobility road map will require a collaborative and phased approach anchored in continuous stakeholder engagement, institutional capacity building, and financial readiness. The following priority actions are recommended:

- **Engagement and feedback:** Engage key stakeholders, including private sector actors, financial institutions, and development partners, to ensure alignment, secure buy-in, and refine the design of proposed initiatives.
- **Detailed and operationalized interventions:** Develop actionable, step-by-step plans for each policy intervention, specifying timelines, resource requirements, institutional responsibilities, and expected outcomes. Define clear coordination mechanisms to ensure accountability across agencies.
- **Capacity building and stakeholder collaboration:** Launch targeted programs to build the capacity of government agencies, local governments, and private sector stakeholders. Strengthen partnerships with private entities to accelerate investments in key areas such as EV infrastructure, public transport electrification, and green logistics.

- **Scaled pilot projects and phased implementation:** Prioritize high-impact interventions, such as national charging infrastructure deployment and the electrification of public transport, in the initial phase. Successful pilots should serve as models for nationwide replication and scaling of medium- and long-term actions.
- **Policy and financial readiness:** Enhance the policy environment through fiscal incentives, carbon pricing, and supportive regulations to attract private sector investment. Align the electrification action plan with Thailand's broader NDC and net-zero targets, and explore co-financing opportunities through international climate finance mechanisms such as Green Climate Fund and Climate Investment Funds to scale up and accelerate investments.

Appendix 3 on the Monitoring and Evaluation Framework is provided to guide implementation and track progress across the programs and measures proposed in the Thailand E-Mobility Mission 2025–2035.

CONCLUSION

Thailand's E-Mobility Mission 2025–2035 sets a clear pathway toward a clean, competitive, and resilient transport future. By integrating public transport modernization, freight electrification, charging infrastructure expansion, domestic manufacturing, and skilling initiatives, the mission positions Thailand as a regional leader in sustainable mobility. Through coordinated policy action, public–private collaboration, and innovative financing mechanisms, Thailand can accelerate its transition to low-carbon transport while advancing its carbon neutrality and net-zero goals. This road map provides not only a framework for decarbonization but also a platform for green growth, job creation, and long-term economic resilience.

A MuvMi driver on an e-tuktuk in a major road in Bangkok (photo by ADB).

APPENDIX 1: POLICY MEASURES UNDER EV 3.0 AND EV 3.5

Thailand's electric vehicle (EV) policy has evolved through successive phases known as EV 3.0 (2022–2024) and EV 3.5 (2024–2027), introduced by the National Electric Vehicle Policy Committee to accelerate zero-emission vehicle adoption and strengthen domestic manufacturing. EV 3.0 focused on stimulating demand through subsidies, tax reductions, and import offsets to kick-start market adoption, while EV 3.5 builds on this foundation by tightening local content rules and promoting long-term industrial competitiveness through supply chain localization and research and development (R&D) incentives.

EV 3.0 (2022–2024): SCALING DOMESTIC DEMAND

Table A1.1: Support Measures Under EV 3.0

EV 3.0	Passenger Cars		Pickup Trucks	Motorcycles
Specification	Price: ≤ B2 million Battery Capacity: 1-30 kWh	Price: ≤ B2 million Battery Capacity: ≥ 30 kWh	Price: ≤ B2 million Battery Capacity: ≥ 30 kWh	Price: ≤ B150,000
Purchase Subsidy	B70,000/Unit	B150,000/Unit	B150,000/Unit	B18,000/Unit
Import Specifications	Price: ≤ B2 million Battery Capacity: ≥ 10 kWh	Price: B2-7 million Battery Capacity: ≥ 30 kWh	Price: ≤ B2 million Battery Capacity: ≥ 30 kWh	Price: ≤ B150,000 Battery Capacity: ≥ 50 kWh
Excise Tax	2% (Reduced from 8%)		0% (Reduced from 10%)	1%
Import Tariff	Up to 40% Reduction	Up to 20% Reduction	No Reduction	No Reduction
BEV Import: BEV Production in Thailand	1: 1 for Production by 2024 1: 1.5 for Production by 2025 (Production compensation must be the same model as imported for passenger cars with price between B2-7 million.)			

BEV = battery electric vehicle, EV = electric vehicle.
Source: S. Choksawatpaisan. 2024. *Thailand Industry outlook 2024-26: E-Vehicle Industry*. Krungsri Research.

DEMAND

- Purchase subsidy for passenger BEVs:
  - » B70,000-B150,000 for imported vehicles costing up to B2 million.
  - » B150,000 for domestically produced e-trucks costing up to B2 million with a battery capacity over 30 kilowatt-hours (kWh).
- B18,000 subsidy for e-motorcycles from eligible manufacturers.
- Reduced import duty charges on BEVs (only passenger cars):
  - » 40% reduction for completely built-up units priced up to B2 million.
  - » 20% reduction for completely built-up units priced up to B7 million. These reductions are applicable until 2025.
- Reduced annual road tax for BEV owners:
  - » 80% reduction for the first year following vehicle registration and applicable until September 2025.

SUPPLY

- Requirements for manufacturers receiving investment support under EV 3.0 are as follows:
  - » Manufacturers importing EVs for the Thai market in 2022 and 2023 must offset imports with domestically produced vehicles in 2024 and 2025.
  - » Manufacturers starting local production in 2024 must match imports on a 1-to-1 basis.
  - » Manufacturers commencing production in 2025 must produce 1.5 vehicles domestically for every imported unit.
- For models with battery capacities under 30 kWh and priced below B2 million:
  - » Manufacturers can offset imports with any BEV model sold domestically.
- For models with battery capacities of 30 kWh or more and priced between B2 million and B7 million:
  - » Manufacturers must produce and distribute only those models that were previously imported.
- Reduced excise duties for passenger EVs seating up to 10 people:
  - » From 1 January 2020 to 31 December 2022: Excise duty rate was 0%.
  - » From 1 January 2023 to 31 December 2025: Excise duty rate is 2% for vehicles endorsed by the Board of Investment (BOI).
  - » Non-BOI-endorsed EVs are subject to an excise duty rate of 8%.
  - » Conventional internal combustion engine (ICE) vehicles have excise duty rates ranging from 25%–40%.

INFRASTRUCTURE

Thailand's BOI enhanced investment incentives and eligibility conditions for charging station developers and operators to expand charging infrastructure and improve service provision.

- Corporate income tax exemption eligibility for investments in charging stations:
  - » 5 years for stations with 40 or more chargers (including 10 direct current [DC] chargers).
  - » 3 years for stations with 16 to fewer than 40 chargers.
- Simplified BOI investment promotion process includes:
  - » Removing ineligibility for additional investment incentives granted by other agencies.
  - » Eliminating the requirement for mandatory ISO certification.
- New requirements for investors:
  - » Compliance with relevant safety regulations.
- Submission of a plan to implement either:
  - » An EV smart charging system, or
  - » Connection to an EV charging network operator platform.[1]

1 BOI. 2023. Inside Thailand's EV Revolution: From luxury cars to tuk-tuks, an electric era dawns.

EV 3.5 (2024–2027): PROMOTING FULL-SCALE DOMESTIC MANUFACTURING CAPABILITIES

Table A1.2: Support Measures Under EV 3.0

EV 3.5	Passenger Cars		Pickup Trucks	Motorcycles
Specification	Price: ≤ B2 million Battery Capacity: 10–50 kWh	Price: ≤ B2 million Battery Capacity: ≥ 50 kWh	Price: ≤ B2 million Battery Capacity: ≥ 50 kWh	Price: ≤ B150,000 Battery Capacity: ≥ 3 kWh
Purchase Subsidy	B50,000/Unit	B100,000/Unit	B100,000/Unit	B10,000/Unit
Import Specifications	Price: ≤ B2 million Battery Capacity: ≥ 10 kWh	Price: Price: B2 million–B7 million Battery Capacity: ≥ 50 kWh	Price: ≤ B2 million Battery Capacity: ≥ 50 kWh	
Excise Tax	2% (Reduced from 8%)		0% (Reduced from 10%) for 2024-25, increasing to 2% thereafter.	No Reduction
Import Tariff	Up to 40% Reduction During 2024-25	Up to 20% Reduction	No Reduction	No Reduction
BEV Import: BEV Production in Thailand	1:2 for Production by 2026 1:3 for Production by 2027 (Production compensation must be the same model as imported for passenger cars with price at over B2 million.)			

BEV = battery electric vehicle, EV = electric vehicle, kWh = kilowatt-hour.
Source: S. Choksawatpaisan. 2024. *Thailand Industry outlook 2024-26: E-Vehicle Industry*. Krungsri Research.

DEMAND

- Purchase subsidy for passenger BEVs:
  - Reduced to B50,000-B100,000 for vehicles priced up to B2 million.
  - B100,000 subsidy for pickups priced up to B2 million with a battery capacity over 50 kWh.
- Subsidies for motorcycles reduced to B10,000 per unit.

SUPPLY

Manufacturers receiving investment support under the EV 3.5 scheme that imported EVs in 2024 and 2025 must offset these imports with domestically produced vehicles in 2026 and 2027:

- Requirements for local production:
  - Manufacturers commencing production in 2026 must produce two domestically manufactured EVs for every imported EV (1:2 ratio).
  - Manufacturers commencing production in 2027 must produce three domestically manufactured EVs for every imported EV (1:3 ratio).
- Companies importing passenger EVs priced above B2 million must manufacture identical models domestically.

Energy Absolute Public Bus Electrification Project (photo by ADB).

OTHER MEASURES

BOI offers tax holidays and additional incentives for joint ventures between Thai and foreign companies manufacturing EV parts. New joint ventures must invest at least B100 million and meet specific ownership requirements.

Additional incentives include:

- Five-year corporate income tax exemptions and duty exemptions on imported machinery and raw materials.
- Nontax incentives for developing EV smart charging systems with at least 40 chargers (including 25% fast chargers). A 3-year tax exemption applies in other cases.
- A 5-year tax exemption for battery swapping stations meeting requirements on procurement plans, safety standards, implementation schedules, and fee collection (covering both service and electricity costs).

APPENDIX 2: GLOBAL AND REGIONAL CASE STUDIES

To address the challenges and opportunities identified in Thailand's electric vehicle (EV) policy framework, this review analyzes global and regional experiences to guide the country's efforts in decarbonizing its transport sector. The analysis covers 10 economies—the People's Republic of China; Germany; India; Indonesia; Japan; the Republic of Korea; Norway; Taipei,China; the United States, and Viet Nam—representing markets at different stages of transition, from advanced to emerging economies. Insights and data from the case studies are as of October 2024.

The review focuses on two core policy areas: (i) the legal and institutional frameworks governing EV adoption, and (ii) support measures that promote EV deployment, including fiscal incentives (such as subsidies and tax rebates) and non-fiscal incentives (such as dedicated lanes or parking privileges). By benchmarking Thailand's policy landscape against these examples, the review identifies global best practices and regional distinctions, offering actionable recommendations to strengthen Thailand's e-mobility strategy.

GLOBAL MARKET

1. PEOPLE'S REPUBLIC OF CHINA	
As of 2023, the EV market of the People's Republic of China (PRC) continued to lead globally, demonstrating significant growth and innovation. Nearly 8.5 million EVs were sold in 2023, reflecting strong domestic demand and government support.[a] The country accounted for about 60% of global e-car sales in 2022 and continues to dominate due to increasing demand (IEA). In the first half of 2023, over 3.65 million new energy vehicles (NEVs) were sold, which stood highest in the global market.[b]	
A. Specific Legislation and Regulations for EVs	
Policy Framework	**Development Plan for EV Industry (2012–2020):** Introduced on 28 June 2012, targeting annual manufacturing capacity of 2 million BEVs and PHEVs by 2020.[c] **Guiding Opinions on EV Adoption (2014):** Released on 14 July 2014, outlining a comprehensive approach to promote EV adoption through infrastructure development, technology innovation, financial support, tax benefits, and government procurement preferences. **Administrative Provisions for Market Access (2017):** On 6 January 2017, the Ministry of Industry, and Information Technology (MIIT) introduced provisions for market access for EV manufacturers and products.[d] **Safety Monitoring for NEVs (2016):** MIIT's 11 November 2016 circular requires NEV manufacturers to establish safety platforms for user consent and monitoring. **Technical standards for subsidies:** The PRC mandates specific technical standards and performance requirements for EVs to qualify for subsidies, including minimum range and energy consumption thresholds.[e]

continued on next page

Table *continued*

B. Measures / Support Schemes to Promote EVs	
Fiscal Incentives	**Incentive grants:** Central and local governments provide subsidies to encourage EV adoption. In 2016, subsidies reached up to RMB100,000 (approx. $15,000) per vehicle, making the PRC's average EV purchase subsidies the second most generous globally, after Norway.[f] **Tax Advantages** **Exemption from vehicle purchase tax:** Available for qualifying EVs. **Catalogs for exemption:** Since 2014, MIIT and SAT have released 16 catalogs specifying eligible EV models for this exemption, with the 16th catalog valid from January 2018 to December 2020. **Exemption from vehicle and vessel tax:** Applies to BEVs and FCEVs; certain PHEVs also qualify. **Eligibility criteria:** PHEVs are eligible for tax exemptions based on factors such as battery charge duration, use of lead-acid batteries, and fuel consumption compared to non-EVs. **Regular updates:** MIIT regularly updates catalogs of qualified EV models. **Diversified Financing Resources** **Encouraging financial innovation:** Financial institutions are encouraged to develop innovative financial products and credit review systems tailored to the EV industry. **Range of financing resources:** These initiatives ensure financial institutions provide resources for EV manufacturing, marketing, and purchases. **Incentivizing financing channels:** EV manufacturers are encouraged to expand financing channels through public offerings, bond issuance, or asset securitization. **Supporting price incentives:** These efforts help EV manufacturers offer price incentives to potential buyers.[g] **Government Financial Support for Charging Infrastructure** **Subsidies for local governments:** The central government offers subsidies to local governments that meet annual EV promotion targets. **Funding areas:** Subsidies are intended for the construction and operation of charging infrastructure, battery-charging and swapping networks, and service improvements.[h] **Restrictions on use:** Local governments are prohibited from using these subsidies as direct purchase grants for EV buyers or subsidies for EV manufacturers.[i]
Non-Fiscal Incentives	**Preferential vehicle registration policies:** Major cities like Shanghai and Beijing use quota systems for vehicle registration. EVs have separate, less competitive quotas, with Shanghai offering free registration plates for qualifying BEVs or PHEVs if the annual quota is not exceeded. **Driving and parking privileges:** In cities like Nanjing and Shanghai, EVs are exempt from restrictions on reserved bus lanes. Many cities also provide designated parking with charging facilities for EVs at public institutions. **Favorable treatment for charging stations:** State Grid of China and China Southern Power Grid offer preferential treatment to commercial charging station operators, exempting them from "basic charges" before 2020. **Incentives for EV buses:** Local governments are encouraged to integrate EVs into public transport, with annual targets for replacing traditional buses with e-buses. Failure to meet these targets results in reduced oil subsidies, indirectly promoting EV bus adoption.[j]

continued on next page

B. Measures / Support Schemes to Promote EVs	
Challenges	**Grid overload risks:** High concentration of EVs in urban centers places pressure on electricity grids. **Battery waste management:** Large-scale recycling and disposal of EV batteries is becoming critical (footnote g). **Air quality disparities:** While EVs reduce urban air pollution, coal-heavy electricity generation limits overall environmental benefits. **Uneven charging network:** Disparity between urban and rural charging infrastructure availability. **Market oversaturation:** Intense competition among numerous EV manufacturers could lead to market instability.

BEV = battery electric vehicle, EV = electric vehicle, FCVE = fuel cell electric vehicle, IEA = International Energy Agency, PHEV = plug-in hybrid electric vehicle, SAT = State Administration of Taxation.

[a] D. Ren. 2023. Chinese EV makers on course to smashing 8.5 million 2023 sales target for mainland, industry players and observers say. *South China Morning Post*. 8 October.

[b] IEA. Global EV Outlook 2024: Trends in e-cars. https://iea.org/reports/global-ev-outlook-2024/trends-in-electric-cars.

[c] Think Blue Data, Energy-saving and new energy automobile industry development plan (2012-2020). https://tinyurl.com/mw3ud4nj.

[d] International Council on Clean Transportation, China's new energy vehicle mandate and implications for the global market. https://tinyurl.com/3vr5e6c5.

[e] International Council on Clean Transportation, China's new energy vehicle policy update. https://theicct.org/wp-content/uploads/2021/06/China-NEV_ICCT_policy-update_17052017_vF.pdf.

[f] BBVA Research. 2023. The Rise of China's EV Sector, and Its Implications for the World. https://bbvaresearch.com/wp-content/uploads/2023/04/The_rise_of_China_s_EV_sector_and_its_implications_for_the_world_WB.pdf.

[g] World Bank. The Role of Government in the Market for E-Vehicles: Evidence from China. https://documents1.worldbank.org/curated/en/776201597325973519/pdf/The-Role-of-Government-in-the-Market-for-Electric-Vehicles-Evidence-from-China.pdf.

[h] ICCT. Assessment of E-Car Promotion Policies in Chinese Cities. https://theicct.org/wp-content/uploads/2021/06/China_city_NEV_assessment_20181018.pdf.

[i] BBVA Research. The Rise of China's EV Sector, and Its Implications for the World, 2023. https://bbvaresearch.com/wp-content/uploads/2023/04/The_rise_of_China_s_EV_sector_and_its_implications_for_the_world_WB.pdf.

[j] ICCT. Assessment of E-Car Promotion Policies in Chinese Cities. https://theicct.org/wp-content/uploads/2021/06/China_city_NEV_assessment_20181018.pdf.

2. GERMANY	
The German EV market has grown rapidly over the last decade; however, total EV sales have begun to slow following subsidy reductions and rising energy costs. In 2023, BEV sales were expected to increase by 8% to 510,000 units, while overall EV sales (including PHEVs) were projected to decline by 8% to 765,000. As a result, the share of e-cars in total registrations was forecast to drop from 31% to 28%, reflecting reduced incentives, slower charging infrastructure expansion, and high electricity prices.[a]	
A. Specific Legislation and Regulations for EVs	
Policy Framework	**Government policies driving EV growth:** The growth in Germany's EV market is driven by government policies that promote e-mobility, including buyer incentives and investments in charging infrastructure, aligned with environmental goals to reduce carbon emissions.[b] **Master Plan Charging Infrastructure II:** Aims to expand EV charging stations nationwide through rapid deployment, digital integration for improved usability, and private sector investment.[c] **Act on E-Mobility (Elektromobilitätsgesetz, 2015):** Enables municipalities to offer preferential parking, reduced rates, and special number plates for EVs, as well as exemptions from traffic restrictions.[d] **Facilitation of private charging stations:** The Federal Council reintroduced provisions easing installation of private charging infrastructure for tenants and apartment owners, granting landlords and co-owners the right to install charging stations. **Act on the Digitalization of the Energy Transition (Gesetz zur Digitalisierung der Energiewende, 2016):** Supports reduced network access fees for suppliers integrating EVs as distributed energy storage, contributing to long-term smart grid development. **Decree on Charging Stations (Ladesäulenverordnung, 2016):** Establishes technical and interoperability standards for public charging stations.[e]

continued on next page

Table *continued*

B. Measures / Support Schemes to Promote EVs	
Fiscal Incentives	**Purchase grants:** The "Umweltbonus" (environmental bonus) program provides up to €9,000 in grants for purchasing or leasing EVs within an eligible registration period.[f] **Vehicle tax exemption:** EVs registered between 2011 and 2030 are exempt from vehicle tax for the first 10 years, with reduced tax thereafter. PHEVs pay tax, but at a lower rate than diesel/gasoline vehicles, based on their lower CO_2 emissions. **Company car tax:** Fully electric company cars priced below €60,000 are taxed at 0.25% of the list price per month, compared to 1% for ICE cars. Hybrid company cars and fully e-cars priced above €60,000 are taxed at 0.5% of the list price per month, compared to 1% for ICE cars. **VAT:** The temporary reduction of VAT to 16% between 1 July and 30 December 2020 has expired and the standard 19% now applies.[g]
Non-Fiscal Incentives	**Driving and parking privileges:** Under the E-Mobility Act (EmoG) federal states and cities may offer EV drivers free or reserved parking spots.[h] **Support for Charging Infrastructure** **€2.5 billion investment:** Allocated for expanding charging infrastructure and battery cell production under the €130 billion national stimulus package.[i] **1 million charging stations by 2030:** National target to support mass EV adoption.[j] **EV charging at gas stations:** Future plans require all gas stations to provide EV charging. **Bus and truck fund:** €1.2 billion (until 2021) allocated to promote e-buses, e-trucks, and charging infrastructure.
Challenges	**Automaker transition:** Established manufacturers face challenges shifting from ICE to EV technologies. **Charging infrastructure gaps:** Insufficient public charging points to meet growing EV demand. **Regulatory hurdles:** Complex permitting processes for setting up new charging stations.[k] **Consumer skepticism:** Concerns over EV range, upfront costs, and charging convenience among traditional car buyers. **Supply chain bottlenecks:** Dependence on imported raw materials like cobalt, lithium, and rare earth elements.[l]

BEV = battery electric vehicle, EV = electric vehicle, ICE = internal combustion engine, PHEV = plug-in hybrid electric vehicle, VAT = value-added tax.

[a] E. Heymann. 2023. Electromobility: Competition for market share intensifies. *Deutsche Bank Research*. 12 July. https://www.dbresearch.com/PROD/RPS_EN-PROD/PROD0000000000528990/Electromobility%3A_Competition_for_market_share_inte.pdf.

[b] Federal Ministry for Economic Affairs and Energy (BMWK), Regulatory Environment and Incentives for Using E-Vehicle.

[c] International Council on Clean Transportation. Germany's Charging Infrastructure Strategy. https://theicct.org.

[d] CMS Law. E-Vehicles in Germany: Legal Overview. https://cms.law.

[e] Alternative Fuels Observatory. E-Mobility Regulation Map. https://alternative-fuels-observatory.ec.europa.eu/.

[f] VDA. Electric vehicle tax in Germany Verband der Automobilindustrie, 2021. https://vda.de/en/topics/economic-policy/taxes/ev-tax.

[g] Wallbox. 2021. EV incentives in Germany. https://blog.wallbox.com/ev-incentives-germany.

[h] BMWK. Regulatory environment and incentives for using e-vehicles. https://bmwk.de/Redaktion/EN/Artikel/Industry/regulatory-environment-and-incentives-for-using-electric-vehicles.html.

[i] IEA. 2020. Sustainable transport and charging station infrastructure. https://iea.org/policies/11554-sustainable-transport-charging-station-infrastructure.

[j] ICCT. 2020. Germany: National charging infrastructure policy. https://theicct.org/wp-content/uploads/2021/06/germany-charging-infrastructure-20201021.pdf.

[k] RVO. German charging infrastructure regulations: A report on the legal framework. https://rvo.nl/sites/default/files/2019/04/German%20charging%20infrastructure%20regulations%20report%20march%202019_0.pdf.

[l] Industrial Europe. 2023. Supply chain risks for the EV industry: Lithium, cobalt, and rare earth elements. https://news.industriall-europe.eu/documents/upload/2023/2/638113042464886188_HIVA_Germany.pdf.

3. INDIA	
The Indian EV market has expanded steadily in recent years, supported by a strong policy push, particularly for 2- and 3-wheelers. EV adoption has been driven by fiscal incentives under the Faster Adoption and Manufacturing of Hybrid and E-Vehicles (FAME) Scheme, reduced taxes, and large-scale electrification programs. India remains one of the fastest-growing EV markets globally, although the pace varies across states due to infrastructure gaps and affordability constraints. India is rapidly advancing its transition to EVs as part of its broader environmental and energy security strategies. With severe air pollution and a growing demand for mobility, the shift toward EVs is seen as a crucial step. The government has implemented a series of policies to foster a conducive ecosystem for EV adoption, emphasizing both demand- and supply-side measures.[a] The initial focus was on creating an enabling policy environment, which led to the launch of the National E-Mobility Mission Plan (NEMMP) 2020 in 2013. This plan established the early framework for increasing EV penetration by addressing national energy security, vehicular pollution, and the expansion of domestic manufacturing capacity. Building on NEMMP, the FAME Scheme was introduced. FAME I and its successor, FAME II, have been instrumental in promoting the production and adoption of electric and hybrid vehicle technologies, with substantial subsidies allocated to e-buses and 2- and 3-wheelers, along with targeted support for private cars. More recently, in response to growing market uptake, India has launched an EV manufacturing policy to attract greater global investment in domestic manufacturing.[b]	
A. Specific Legislation and Regulations for EVs	
Policy Framework	**Department of Heavy Industries (DHI):** Within the Ministry of Heavy Industries and Public Enterprises (MOHIPE), the DHI leads national efforts to accelerate EV adoption. **FAME Scheme (2015):** The FAME Scheme was notified in March 2015, focusing on four major areas: Technology Development, Demand Incentives, Charging Infrastructure, and Pilot Projects. **FAME Scheme Phase I (2015–2019):** Phase I ran from 2015 to 31 March 2019 with a budget of INR8.95 bilion. It supported technological development, demand generation, pilot projects, and charging infrastructure.[c] **FAME Scheme Phase II (2019–2024):** Phase II was launched in April 2019 and continued until March 2024, with several amendments. Key updates include the following. » **Increased incentives for electric 2-wheelers:** Raised from INR10,000 per kilowatt-hour (kWh) to INR15,000/kWh, with the maximum cap increased from 20%–40% of the vehicle cost. » **Demand aggregation for electric 3-wheelers:** Energy Efficiency Services Limited will aggregate demand for 300,000 electric 3-wheelers across multiple user segments to reduce up-front costs and match those of internal combustion engine (ICE) 3-wheeler. » **Transition to e-buses in major cities:** Nine cities (with populations over 4 million, i.e., Mumbai, Delhi, Bengaluru, Hyderabad, Ahmedabad, Chennai, Kolkata, Surat, and Pune) were initially prioritized for transition to e-buses and later expanded nationwide, with a target to deploy 50,000 e-buses. The government has adopted a demand aggregation model for centralized procurement through a government agency. This model has substantially reduced e-bus costs in total-cost-of-ownership terms, with CESL's aggregated procurement under Gross Cost Contract/OPEX arrangements delivering significant savings.[d] » **Connectivity and safety of EV charging stations:** The Central Electricity Authority under the Ministry of Power issued regulations in February 2019 for the connectivity of EV charging stations to the electricity system below the 33-kilovolt voltage level. These form part of the Technical Standards for Connectivity of Distributed Generation Resources Amendment Regulations and the Safety and Electric Supply Regulations, 2019.[e] » **Charging infrastructure:** The Ministry of Power has issued guidelines for EV charging infrastructure, and the Bureau of Energy Efficiency serves as the Central Nodal Agency. The MOHIPE amended building by-laws to require residential and commercial complexes to allocate 20% of parking spaces for EV charging facilities.

continued on next page

Table *continued*

	» **Vehicle Scrappage Policy (2021):** Scrapping center offers 4%-6% of a vehicle's ex-showroom price as scrap value. States have been advised to provide a 25% road tax rebate for personal vehicles and 15% for commercial vehicles. This policy boosts the availability of low-cost raw materials for the auto steel and electronics industries. Additionally, the government imposes a 10%–15% "Green Tax" on private vehicle registration renewals after 15 years.[f] » **State-level policies:** Several Indian states have developed EV policies that align with national goals, offering additional subsidies, mandates for EV adoption in public transport, and incentives for local EV manufacturing. States like Karnataka, Tamil Nadu, and Maharashtra have attracted investments by providing tailored incentives such as tax rebates, lower electricity rates for EV charging, and capital subsidies to attract EV and battery manufacturing investments.[g]
B. Measures / Support Schemes to Promote EVs	
Fiscal Incentives	**Tax rebate:** In 2019, the Ministry of Finance reduced the goods and services tax (GST) on EV purchases from 12% to 5%, streamlined customs duties, and introduced a INR150,000 income tax rebate for EV investments to support the "Make in India" initiative.[h] **Duty reduction:** Nickel manganese cobalt is essential for lithium-ion batteries. Custom charges on nickel ore and nickel oxide will be zero, whereas ferro nickel will be reduce from 15% to 2.5%. Reducing costumes duty on motor parts from 10% to 7.5% will assist in reducing overall costs. **PM E-Bus Sewa:** The Ministry of Housing and Urban Affairs launched the "PM E-Bus Sewa" Scheme to add 10,000 e-buses to city operations under a public–private partnership model, with an estimated cost of INR576.13 billion, including INR2 quintillion from the central government.[i] **Reduced GST:** The GST on EVs has been lowered to 5%, compared to 28% on conventional vehicles. **Income tax deductions:** Buyers of EVs can claim income tax deductions on loans taken to purchase EVs.[j]
Non-Fiscal Incentives	**Green license plates:** Distinctive green license plates for EVs offer advantages such as preferred parking and exemption from toll charges in some regions. **Subsidies for manufacturers:** Subsidies and support for EV and battery manufacturers to set up facilities in India.
Challenges	**Insufficient charging infrastructure:** Slow rollout of public charging stations. **High battery costs:** Dependence on imported batteries inflates EV prices. **Range anxiety:** Consumers fear limited driving range due to inadequate charging networks. **State-level variances:** Uneven implementation of EV policies across states. **Grid reliability and energy source:** Ensuring clean electricity for EV charging.[k]

EV = electric vehicle, OPEX = operational expenditure.

[a] NITI Aayog. 2013. National E-Mobility Mission Plan 2020. Government of India.
[b] TERI. E-Vehicle Policy and Manufacturing Framework in India, 2023.
[c] Government of India, MOHIPE. Faster Adoption and Manufacturing of Hybrid and E-Vehicles (FAME India) Scheme - Phase 1, 2015.
[d] Government of India, MOHIPE. Faster Adoption and Manufacturing of Hybrid and E-Vehicles (FAME India) Scheme - Phase 2, 2019.
[e] CEA. 2019. Technical Standards for Connectivity of EV Charging Stations. February.
NITI Aayog. 2021. *Handbook for EV Charging Infrastructure Implementation.* https://niti.gov.in/sites/default/files/2021-08/HandbookforEVChargingInfrastructureImplementation081221.pdf.
[f] Vehicle Scrappage Policy in India, 2023.
[g] WRI Cities, E-Vehicle State Policy.
[h] Government of India Ministry of Finance. Union Budget 2019-2020. https://indiabudget.gov.in/budget2019-20/doc/bh1.pdf.
[i] PM eBus Sewa Guidelines.
[j] Government of India, GST Council. GST Rates for E-Vehicles and Related Items, 2020. https://gstcouncil.gov.in/cgst-rate-notification?page=8.
[k] World Bank. 2021. *E-Mobility in India: Accelerating Implementation.* https://documents1.worldbank.org/curated/en/772841622724981757/pdf/Electric-Mobility-in-India-Accelerating-Implementation.pdf.

4. JAPAN	
Japan is steadily advancing its EV transition as part of its long-term environmental goals. Record EV sales in 2022 reflect growing consumer uptake alongside sustained policy support. The government is strengthening the EV ecosystem through charging infrastructure development, regulatory reforms, and commitments to carbon neutrality by 2050. As a major automotive hub, Japan continues to develop a broad range of EV technologies for domestic and international markets.[a]	
A. Specific Legislation and Regulations for EVs	
Policy Framework	**Basic Policy for Economic and Fiscal Management and Reform (2023, 16 June):** Sets Japan's strategy to support carbon neutrality, including transitioning to zero-emission vehicles (ZEVs) by 2035.[b] **Guidelines for Promoting the Development of EV Charging Infrastructure (2023, 18 October):** Issued by the Ministry of Economy, Trade and Industry to enhance charging convenience and promote the development of charging networks across Japan.[c] **Environmental and Energy Policy (2024):** Reinforces decarbonization efforts with EVs as a central pillar to these goals.[d]
B. Measures / Support Schemes to Promote EVs	
Fiscal Incentives	**Subsidies for EV purchases:** Financial support for the purchase of EVs, with grants for both individuals and businesses.[e] **EV purchase tax exemptions:** Exemption from road tax for EVs to encourage their purchase.[f] **Charging infrastructure support:** Incentives are offered for the installation of EV charging stations.[g]
Non-Fiscal Incentives	**ZEV emission standards:** Stringent emission standards for new vehicles incentivize manufacturers to shift toward producing electric and other ZEVs.[h] **Access to EV-only zones:** Certain urban areas offer reduced restrictions and benefits like preferential parking for EVs. **Collaborations and partnerships:** The government facilitates public–private partnerships to build EV infrastructure and encourage the use of EVs.[i]
Challenges	**Consumer preference for hybrids:** Strong loyalty to hybrid vehicles delays full transition to EVs. **Charging infrastructure:** Insufficient and fragmented public charging network. **High energy costs:** Electricity costs make EV charging less economical compared to fossil fuels.[j] **Battery manufacturing lag:** Limited domestic production of EV batteries compared to competitors like the PRC. **Grid modernization:** Challenges in integrating EV charging with an aging power grid system.[k]

EV = electric vehicle, PRC = People's Republic of China.

[a] Y. Chu and H. Cui. 2023. Annual update on the global transition to electric vehicles: 2022. International Council on Clean Transportation. https://theicct.org/wp-content/uploads/2023/06/Global-EV-sales-2022_FINAL.pdf.

[b] Cabinet Office of Japan, Basic Policy for Economic and Fiscal Management and Reform. 2023. https://www5.cao.go.jp/keizai-shimon/kaigi/cabinet/honebuto/2023/2023_basicpolicies_en.pdf.

[c] Ministry of Economy, Trade, and Industry (METI). Guidelines for Promoting the Development of EV Charging Infrastructure. https://meti.go.jp/english/press/2023/1018_002.html.

[d] Japan Fair Trade Commission. Environmental and Energy Policy. https://jftc.go.jp/en/pressreleases/yearly-2024/May/240529.html.

[e] METI. Subsidies for EV Purchases. https://enecho.meti.go.jp/en/category/special/article/detail_199.html.

[f] IEA. Eco-Car Tax Break and Subsidies for Vehicles. https://iea.org/policies/13826-eco-car-tax-break-and-subsidies-for-vehicles.

[g] METI. Subsidies for EV Purchases. https://enecho.meti.go.jp/en/category/special/article/detail_199.html.

[h] Japan's Zero-Emission Vehicle Standards.

[i] R. Bharadwaj. 2023. The Rise of Electric Vehicles in Japan: An Exploration of Market Trends. Blog.23 October. Bolt.Earth. https://bolt.earth/blog/japan-ev-market?srsltid=AfmBOoqLX985ZGhUYiwl6gLEuw9H60S33su5ZS2d4Cfc28UY8PEEfueFutm_source.

[j] McKinsey Company. 2023. Profiling Japan's early EV adopters. https://mckinsey.com/~/media/mckinsey/dotcom/client_service/Automotive%20and%20Assembly/PDFs/Profiling_Japans_early_EV_adopters.ashx.

[k] MIT Center for Energy and Environmental Policy Research. 2024. Electric vehicles, and electricity costs in Japan. https://ceepr.mit.edu/wp-content/uploads/2024/10/MIT-CEEPR-WP-2024-16.pdf.

5. REPUBLIC OF KOREA	
The Republic of Korea (ROK), a major player in the global auto industry, has been rapidly transitioning toward EVs to combat climate change and reduce dependence on fossil fuels. The country's robust technological ecosystem, led by companies such as Hyundai, has supported significant advancements in EV technology and manufacturing. As per recent data, the ROK has seen a sharp increase in EV sales, attributed to expanding consumer acceptance and supportive government policies. The country recorded over 52,000 EV units sold in 2020, a significant rise from previous years. Forecasts suggest continued growth, with electric and hybrid vehicles expected to account for more than 30% of the domestic auto market by 2030.[a]	
A. Specific Legislation and Regulations for EVs	
Policy Framework	The government has implemented a range of policy measures to support the EV transition, including purchase subsidies, tax reductions, and investments in research and development (R&D). These policies are designed to reduce the cost barrier for consumers and businesses and to promote domestic EV production capabilities.
B. Measures / Support Schemes to Promote EVs	
Fiscal Incentives	**EV purchase incentives:** Tax reductions, subsidies covering up to 50% of the EV price cap, and reduced electricity rates for EV charging during off-peak hours.[b] **15% tax credit for EV investment:** Includes fuel cell subsidies of W70 million (~$53,800) in national funds and W40 million (~$30,700) in local funds. **Liquidity support and loan guarantees for domestic manufacturers** **Increased EV subsidy:** Raised from a maximum of W6.8 million (~$5,200) to W7.8 million (~$6,000), depending on manufacturer price discounts, for EVs with maximum base price of W57 million (~$43,800). **Consumption tax discount:** Up to W3 million (~$2,300) for BEVs and W4 million (~$3,100) for FCEVs.
Non-Fiscal Incentives	The ROK has implemented various non-fiscal incentives such as exemptions from tolls, reduced parking fees, and access to bus lanes for EVs.
Challenges	**High costs:** High production and battery costs limit affordability. **Urban charging challenges:** Lack of space for installing charging stations in dense urban areas. **Dependence on imports:** Heavy reliance on imported key raw materials for battery manufacturing. **Market fagmentation:** Intense competition among domestic and international EV manufacturers creates market inefficiencies. **Regulatory alignment:** Need for cohesive policies aligning EV deployment with renewable energy expansion.[c]

BEV = battery electric vehicle, EV = electric vehicle, FCEV = fuel cell electric vehicle.

[a] Statista. 2023. E-Vehicles in South Korea. https://statista.com/topics/6322/electric-vehicles-in-south-korea.

[b] Korea.net. E-Vehicle and Charging Infrastructure Incentives 2025. https://korea.net/Government/Briefing-Room/Press-Releases/view?articleId=1627030insttCode=A260112type=N.

[c] H. Kim. 2024. Impact of policy incentives on adoption of e-vehicles in South Korea. *KDI Focus*. No. 135, Korea Development Institute. https://doi.org/10.22740/kdi.focus.e.2024.35.

6. NORWAY	
Norway is a global leader in EV adoption, with the highest per capita number of e-cars worldwide. As of 2023, there were over 400,000 e-cars on Norwegian roads, and EVs represented over 60% of new car sales in recent years. In 2020, Norway became the first country where e-cars accounted for over 50% of new car sales. Currently, 15.9% of the total vehicle fleet consists of ZEVs. Supported by abundant hydroelectric power and a robust incentive program, Norway also features 17,000 charging plugs as of 2021, ensuring continued growth in EV adoption.[a]	
A. Specific Legislation and Regulations for EVs	
Policy Framework	**Zero Emissions by 2025 Goal:** All new cars sold by 2025 must be zero-emission (electric or hydrogen). As of 2022, BEVs made up over 20% of registered cars and held a 79.2% market share. The rapid transition is supported by policy instruments and incentives. **National tax system:** Implementation of the "polluter pays" principle, with taxes based on weight, CO_2 emissions, and NOx emissions. High-emission vehicles face higher taxes, while low-emission and zero-emission vehicles receive significant tax reductions. **Energy and decarbonization fund:** Enova, a state-owned enterprise, covers up to 40% of incremental costs for zero-emission transport transitions.[b] **Charging infrastructure:** The government reduces economic risks for charging station investors and supports the establishment of fast-chargers approximately every 50 km on main roads, reducing range anxiety and supporting BEV market expansion by increasing total miles driven.[c]
B. Measures / Support Schemes to Promote EVs	
Fiscal Incentives	**VAT exemption:** E-car sales are exempt from VAT. **Purchase tax exemption:** EV owners are exempt from purchase tax when buying or leasing a new or pre-owned EV. **Road traffic insurance tax:** EV owners are exempt from the annual road traffic insurance tax. **Company car tax discount:** EV owners receive a discount on company car tax depending on the year of manufacture. **Toll discounts:** EV owners are charged a maximum of 50% of standard toll prices on roads and ferries. **Parking fee discounts:** Municipalities set parking fees, but EV owners cannot be charged more than 50% of standard parking costs.[d]
Non-Fiscal Incentives	Access to most bus and taxi lanes, subject to local restrictions. Additionally, the government offers local incentives such as free parking and charging in cities such as Oslo, Fredrikstad, Baerum, and Trondheim.[e]
Challenges	**Grid challenges:** Increasing load on the power grid, especially in urban areas, due to high EV charging demand. **Rural access:** Limited charging infrastructure in remote or rural areas despite a nationwide push. **EV incentive dependency:** Heavy reliance on government subsidies, making the EV market vulnerable if incentives are scaled back. **Battery recycling:** Growing need for EV battery recycling systems. **Cold climate issues:** Reduced battery performance in extreme cold weather, affecting driving range and charging efficiency.[f]

BEV = battery electric vehicle, CO_2 = carbon dioxide, EV = electric vehicle, km = kilometer, NOx = nitrogen oxide, ZEV = zero-emission vehicle.

[a] Statista. Electric vehicles in Norway, 2024. https://statista.com/outlook/mmo/electric-vehicles/norway.
[b] Norwegian Electric. Vehicle Association, Norwegian EV policy. https://elbil.no/english/norwegian-ev-policy.
[c] IEA. Norway 2022 energy policy review. https://iea.blob.core.windows.net/assets/de28c6a6-8240-41d9-9082-a5dd65d9f3eb/NORWAY2022.pdf.
[d] IEA. Norway's e-vehicle incentives, 2023. https://iea.org/policies/17809-norways-electric-vehicle-incentives.
[e] Wallbox. Norway EV incentives. https://blog.wallbox.com/norway-ev-incentives.
[f] IEA. Global EV outlook 2024: Outlook for battery and energy demand. https://iea.org/reports/global-ev-outlook-2024/outlook-for-battery-and-energy-demand.

7. TAIPEI,CHINA	
Taipei,China's EV market is on an upward trajectory, driven by the government's commitment to green transport solutions. The market is dominated by e-scooters, which have become increasingly popular in urban areas due to Taipei,China's dense population and high levels of scooter use. The government has been promoting EV adoption through fiscal and non-fiscal incentives, such as subsidies for electric 2-wheelers and the installation of battery swapping stations. Taipei,China's transition to EVs also includes investment in local manufacturing capabilities, especially for electric components and batteries, with companies like Yulon Motors and Gogoro playing leading roles. As part of its long-term goals, Taipei,China aims to replace traditional gasoline scooters with electric models across its islands by 2027, while expanding sustainable energy solutions to power its growing EV fleet.	
A. Specific Legislation and Regulations for EVs	
Policy Framework	**Green Transportation Action Plan:** Supports transition of public transport (buses, taxis) to ZEVs and promotes widespread adoption of e-scooters in urban areas.[a] **Zero-emission scooter strategy:** Targets 100% electrification of scooters by 2035 supported by battery leasing and swapping networks. **Low-carbon city programs:** Introduces LEZs in metropolitan areas and promotes smart public transport and car-sharing networks.[b] **National energy and carbon reduction plan:** Aims to decarbonize transport as part of Taipei,China's 2050 net-zero target including development of renewable energy-powered charging stations. **Public procurement policies:** Prioritizes EVs in government fleets and public transport, supporting local EV manufacturing. **Legislative support:** Renewable Energy Development Act ensures clean energy for EVs and establishes regulations for EV battery recycling and reducing lifecycle emissions.
B. Measures / Support Schemes to Promote EVs	
Fiscal Incentives	**Commodity tax exemptions:** EV buyers are exempt from the commodity tax until December 2025, applicable up to NT$1.4 million of the vehicle's value, with partial exemptions for higher-priced vehicles. **Subsidies:** Financial subsidies are available for purchasing electric scooters and cars, especially domestically produced EVs.
Non-Fiscal Incentives	Priority lanes and parking spaces for EVs. Deployment of charging stations in public and private spaces. Restrictions on fossil-fuel scooters in urban zones to encourage EV adoption.[c]
Challenges	**Slow adoption of e-cars:** While e-scooters dominate, e-car adoption lags behind. **Battery recycling concerns:** Managing environmental impacts from used EV batteries. **Charging infrastructure expansion:** Efforts to expand infrastructure are progressing slowly. **High consumer costs:** Despite subsidies, EVs remain expensive for many consumers.[d]

EV = electric vehicle, LEZ = low-emission zone, ZEV = zero-emission vehicle.

[a] National Development Council, Green Transportation Action Plan.

[b] Global Covenant of Mayors for Climate Energy. City of New Taipei: Climate Action Plan. https://globalcovenantofmayors.org/wp-content/uploads/2015/09/City-of-New-Taipei-Climate-Action-Plan-1.pdf.

[c] International Trade Administration. Market Intelligence update on E-Vehicles and Charging Stations. 08/07/2023.

[d] Integrated Transport Planning. EV Market Analysis 2023.

8. UNITED STATES	
The United States (US) continues to prioritize EVs as part of its environmental and energy policies aimed at reducing carbon emissions and promoting sustainable energy use. This transition is supported by technological advancements, growing consumer acceptance, and significant support from federal and state governments. The US EV market remains one of the largest globally, driven by innovative companies and a favorable regulatory environment.[a] In 2023, EV sales in the US reached approximately 1.4 million units, a significant increase from nearly 1 million in 2022. This surge elevated the EV market share to about 9% of total new car sales, up from 6.8% in 2022. By the end of 2023, there were over 4 million EVs on US roads, reflecting the growing adoption of EVs nationwide.[b] As of early 2024, the US had more than 55,000 public charging station locations, encompassing Level 2 and direct current fast-charging stations. This expansion has been crucial in supporting the increasing number of EVs and addressing consumer concerns about range anxiety. California continues to lead in EV adoption, with approximately 1.25 million e-vehicle registrations in 2023. Other states with significant EV penetration include Florida, with about 254,878 registrations, and Texas.[c] These developments highlight the US' commitment to advancing e-mobility and reducing its carbon footprint through widespread EV adoption.	
A. Specific Legislation and Regulations for EVs	
Policy Framework	The government has introduced policies to accelerate EV adoption, including subsidies for purchases, grants for charging infrastructure, and emissions regulations that encourage automakers to shift to electric models. Key legislative measures include the E-Vehicle Freedom Act, which focuses on building a nationwide high-speed charging network, and climate legislation aimed at reducing fossil fuel dependence. Key policy measures include: **Bipartisan Infrastructure Law:** Provides significant resources for transport projects, especially EV infrastructure. Includes provisions for electrifying rural transit and school buses and marks a transformative federal investment in US EV charging infrastructure.[d] **Transport and Climate Initiative:** In 2020, over 100 companies, investors, and institutions urged 12 US governors and the DC mayor to sign a memorandum of understanding. Funds transport and EV programs through a cap-and-reinvestment system on fuel emissions. A portion of funds is directed to underserved communities for equitable access. **Transportation Infrastructure Financing and Innovation Act:** Provides federal credit assistance for eligible transport projects, including EV activities. Projects must have a capital cost of at least $50 million ($15 million for ITS projects). Collaborates with DOT funding programs to support EV-related financial needs.[e] **National Highway Performance Program:** Allocates funding to help states meet national highway performance goals and includes support for installing EV charging infrastructure. **Congestion Mitigation and Air Quality Improvement Program:** Provides funds to states and local governments for transport projects under the Clean Air Act. Supports EV acquisitions, engine conversions, and charging infrastructure construction to achieve energy security and eco-friendly goals. **National Highway Freight Program:** Supports the planning and development of road maps for EV charging infrastructure and related projects. **National E-Vehicle Infrastructure Formula Program:** Provides funding for deploying EV charging stations and creating an interconnected network. Supports construction and installation of chargers, parking facilities, utilities, and engine conversions (footnote e).

continued on next page

Table *continued*

B. Measures / Support Schemes to Promote EVs	
Fiscal Incentives	**Federal tax credit:** Up to $7,500 for purchasing new e-vehicles, depending on battery capacity and manufacturer eligibility. This credit phases out once a manufacturer reaches 200,000 EVs sold.[f] **State-level incentives:** Various states offer additional rebates, tax credits, sales tax exemptions, and registration fee waivers to further reduce the cost of purchasing EVs. Some states also provide incentives for EV charging equipment installation. For example, California's Clean Vehicle Rebate Project offers rebates up to $7,000 depending on income and vehicle type.[g] **EV charging infrastructure tax credits:** Under the Inflation Reduction Act (2022), consumers can receive a tax credit of up to 30% of the cost (up to $1,000) for installing EV charging stations at home. Grants are also available for businesses and local governments to install public charging stations.[h] **Commercial and business incentives:** Tax incentives for businesses to adopt EVs and install charging infrastructure, including up to 30% in tax credits for installing commercial charging stations (up to $100,000). The Qualified Plug-in Electric Drive Motor Vehicle Credit allows businesses to claim a credit for EV purchases, including fleet vehicles.[i] **ZEV incentives:** Federal and state governments offer incentives and grants for purchasing ZEVs (electric, hydrogen, or plug-in hybrid vehicles) for both personal and fleet use.[j]
Non-Fiscal Incentives	Non-fiscal incentives include access to carpool lanes for single-occupancy EVs and preferred parking in some cities and states. There are also various grants and funding opportunities for businesses and municipalities to build charging infrastructure.
Challenges	The US EV market faces significant challenges in its charging infrastructure, as detailed in the Harvard Business School report: **Inconsistent charging stations:** About 22% of EV charging stations are out of service, affecting reliability and accessibility for EV owners. **Maintenance problems:** Many stations suffer from frequent functionality issues, leading to concerns over the dependability of charging options during long trips. **Lack of standardization:** Charging stations use different payment systems, connector types, and charging speeds, making the user experience less convenient. **Need for investment:** Significant investment is still required to expand the charging network, especially in rural and underserved areas, to support the increasing number of EVs.[k]

DC = District of Columbia, DOT= Department of Transportation, EV = electric vehicle, ITS = Intelligent Transportation Systems, ZEV = zero-emission vehicle.

[a] Alliance for Automotive Innovation. 2023. Electric vehicle quarterly report 2023. https://autosinnovate.org.
[b] US Department of Energy. 2024. Electric vehicle infrastructure trends. https://afdc.energy.gov/data/10962.
[c] ICCT. 2023. Assessment of US e-vehicle market share and infrastructure trends. https://theicct.org.
[d] Federal Highway Administration. 2023. Electric vehicles and infrastructure under the Bipartisan Infrastructure Law. https://fhwa.dot.gov/bipartisan-infrastructure-law/evs.cfm.
[e] American Public Transportation Association (APTA). 2022. Federal Highway Administration guidance on e-vehicle infrastructure. https://apta.com.
[f] US Department of Transportation. 2023). National E-Vehicle Infrastructure (NEVI) Program Annual Report: 2022-2023. https://driveelectric.gov/files/nevi-annual-report-2022-2023.pdf.
[g] US Internal Revenue Service. 2023. Credits for new clean vehicles purchased in 2023 or after. https://irs.gov/credits-deductions/credits-for-new-clean-vehicles-purchased-in-2023-or-after.
[h] US Department of Energy. Alternative fuels data center: Electric vehicle incentives. https://afdc.energy.gov/fuels/laws/ELEC?state=US.
[i] Electrification Coalition. 2022. The path to electrification: Expanding EV charging infrastructure. https://electrificationcoalition.org/wp-content/uploads/2022/08/SAFE_1-sheet_Webinar.pdf.
[j] CRS. 2021. Electric vehicle incentives: An overview of the federal tax credit for new EVs. https://crsreports.congress.gov/product/pdf/IF/IF12600.
[k] ICCT. 2014. State e-vehicle incentives: A summary of key programs in the US. https://theicct.org/sites/default/files/publications/ICCT_state-EV-incentives_20141030.pdf.

REGIONAL MARKET

9. INDONESIA	
Indonesia, with its significant natural resources including nickel reserves critical for EV batteries, is strategically positioned to be a major player in the EV sector. The government aims to leverage these resources to boost its economy and reduce urban air pollution from the dense traffic. Indonesia's EV market is at an early stage, but growth is expected to accelerate rapidly due to increasing government support and investment in EV manufacturing. Projections suggest that by 2030, a substantial percentage of vehicles on Indonesian roads could be electric, especially in public transport and 2-wheeler segments.[a]	
A. Specific Legislation and Regulations for EVs	
Policy Framework	The government's road map for accelerating EV adoption, outlined in the Minister of Industry Regulation No. 6 of 2022, presents key investment and collaboration opportunities supported by the following core regulations: **Umbrella Law** (Presidential Regulation No. 55/2019): Aimed at accelerating BEV programs through coordinated efforts by the Central and Local Governments to strengthen the EV ecosystem.[b] **Charging infrastructure** (Minister for Energy and Mineral Resources Regulation No. 13/2020): Focuses on developing charging station infrastructure for BEVs used in road transport.[c] **Government fleet transition** (Presidential Instruction No. 7/2022): Mandates the use of BEVs as operational service vehicles for government agencies, signaling strong public-sector commitment to EV adoption. **Regional Action Plan - Bali** (Bali Governor Regulation No. 48/2019): Outlines the region's initiatives for accelerating BEV adoption in Bali, contributing to localized EV ecosystem development.
B. Measures / Support Schemes to Promote EVs	
Fiscal Incentives	**Reduced import duties** on EVs and parts, and tax incentives for EV buyers and businesses investing in EV technology and infrastructure. **Decreased VAT:** 1% for EVs with >40% domestic components and 6% for those with 20%–40%, and VAT exemption on raw materials for batteries (e.g., nickel) and imported EV production equipment. **Zero-percent import duty:** On incompletely knocked-down EVs (announced in 2022). **2020/2021:** Subsidy for electricity used for EV charging, with 30% discounts for home charging between 10 p.m. to 5 a.m. Tax deduction of up to 300% for R&D and technological innovations related to EVs. Maximum 10% tax on the transfer of EVs from manufacturers to owners.[d] **2023:** ~$500 subsidy for E2Ws and ~$5,300 for E4Ws. **2024:** ~$200 million subsidies to boost EV sales and ICE conversions.
Non-Fiscal Incentives	Non-fiscal incentives feature measures like exemption from odd-even license plate regulations, free parking for EVs, and access to special lanes on roads and highway.
Challenges	**High dependence on fossil fuels:** The power grid is coal-dependent, limiting environmental benefits of EVs. **Infrastructure gaps:** Insufficient charging infrastructure, especially outside urban centers. **High initial costs:** EV costs remain higher compared to ICE vehicles despite government incentives.[e]

BEV = battery electric vehicle, E2W = electric 2-wheeled vehicle, E4W = electric 4-wheeled vehicle, EV = electric vehicle, ICE = internal combustion engine, R&D = research and development, VAT = value added tax.

[a] ICCT. 2024. Indonesia's E-Vehicle Policy and Regulatory Landscape. https://theicct.org/wp-content/uploads/2024/07/Indonesia-regs-Policy-Brief- A4-70117-v4.pdf.

[b] Legalink. Incentives for E-Vehicle Importers and Assemblers. https://legalink.ch/xms/files/Incentives_for_Electirc_Vehicle_Importers___Assemblers.pdf.

[c] Climate Laws, Presidential Regulation 55/2019 on E-Vehicles. https://climate-laws.org/document/presidential-regulation-55-2019-on-electric-vehicles_411d.

[d] A. Little. 2023. Indonesia's E-Mobility Potential. https://adlittle.com/sites/default/files/reports/ADL_Indonesias_emobility_potential_2023.pdf.

[e] ICCT. 2024. Indonesia's EV Infrastructure and Environmental Impact. https://theicct.org/wp-content/uploads/2024/02/ID-88-Indonesia-charging_final2.pdf.

10. VIET NAM	
Viet Nam's EV market is in its early stages but is experiencing rapid growth, fueled by both domestic and international interest. The government has identified the EV sector as a key component of its broader environmental and energy strategies, aiming to reduce pollution, improve energy efficiency, and contribute to climate change mitigation goals. While the government has introduced some initiatives, the market remains challenged by limited EV infrastructure, consumer awareness, and high costs compared to traditional vehicles.[a]	
A. Specific Legislation and Regulations for EVs	
Policy Framework	Viet Nam's government has been promoting EV adoption through its broader sustainable development strategies, focusing on green growth, climate change, and environmental protection. Key initiatives include: **Resolution 55/NQ/TW (2020):** National strategy promoting e-mobility and energy storage, aligned with global trends. **Decision 1095/QĐ-BGTVT (2021):** Strategy to develop environmentally friendly vehicles, led by the Transport Development Institute. **Paris Agreement (2020):** Viet Nam committed to reducing GHG emissions, with EV adoption expected to play a key role in the transport sector. **Green growth strategies:** Cities like Ha Noi and Nha Trang have set specific EV adoption targets, such as 5% e-motorcycles by 2030 in Ha Noi and 200 e-buses by 2025 in Nha Trang. **National Automobile Development Strategy (2021-2050):** Sets long-term goals for domestic EV production, including a target of 3.5 million EVs by 2040.[b]
B. Measures / Support Schemes to Promote EVs	
Fiscal Incentives	Viet Nam's fiscal incentives for EV adoption include several tax reductions and exemptions to encourage both production and consumption of EVs: **Excise tax reduction:** EVs benefit from excise tax reductions between 1%–3% for a period of 5 years starting from 2022. **Registration fee exemption:** BEVs are exempt from registration fees for the first 3 years, with a 50% reduction for the following 2 years.[c] **VAT reductions:** The government has implemented VAT cuts for BEVs and associated products.[d]
Non-Fiscal Incentives	Non-fiscal incentives feature measures like exemptions from traffic restrictions and congestion charges in urban areas. Preferential parking for EVs, exemptions from vehicle registration and road taxes, and access to special traffic lanes.
Challenges	**Insufficient charging infrastructure:** Limited charging stations hinder EV adoption.[e] **High costs of EVs:** EVs remain unaffordable for a large portion of the population. **Low consumer awareness:** Lack of public knowledge about EV benefits. **Policy implementation issues:** Challenges in translating policies into actionable results.[f]

BEV = battery electric vehicle, EV = electric vehicle, GHG = greenhouse gas.

[a] World Resources Institute. E-Mobility Roadmap. Viet Nam Case Studies. https://wri.org/research/electric-mobility-roadmap-vietnam-case-studies.

[b] International Trade Administration. Viet Nam E-Vehicle Industry. https://trade.gov/market-intelligence/vietnam-electric-vehicle-industry.

[c] World Resources Institute. E-Mobility Roadmap. Viet Nam Case Studies. https://wri.org/research/electric-mobility-roadmap-vietnam-case-studies.

[d] ICCT. Promoting Development of E-Vehicles in Viet Nam. https://theicct.org/wp-content/uploads/2022/12/asia-pacific-evs-promoting-development-evs-vietnam-dec22-2.pdf.

[e] World Bank. Recommends Pathways for Transitioning to E-Mobility in Viet Nam. https://worldbank.org/en/news/press-release/2024/11/22/world-bank-report-recommends-pathways-for-transitioning-to-electric-mobility-in-viet-nam.

[f] ADB. 2024. Final Report on Sustainable Mobility and Green Transportation in Viet Nam. https://adb.org/sites/default/files/project-documents/55327/55327-002-tacr-en.pdf.

KEY INSIGHTS AND LESSONS FROM CASE STUDIES

Table A2 provides expanded details on the strategies summarized in the main report, presenting economy-specific demand-side, supply-side, and infrastructure measures that have successfully advanced e-mobility transitions worldwide. It consolidates practical policy examples and implementation mechanisms that can inform Thailand's ongoing efforts to strengthen its EV ecosystem and achieve its 2035 e-mobility targets.

Table A2: Summary of Key Strategies and Measures from Global and Regional EV Case Studies

Economy	Demand-Side Measures	Supply-Side Measures	Infrastructure Development
People's Republic of China	• Development Plan for EV Industry (2012-2020): Targeted 2 million BEVs and PHEVs annually by 2020. • Subsidies: Up to $15,000/vehicle (2016). • Market dominance: 60% of global EV sales in 2022; 8.5 million EVs sold (2023). • Quota-free registration plates for EVs in key cities like Shanghai and Beijing.	• Subsidies tied to technical standards: Includes minimum range and energy consumption. • Investment in lithium-ion batteries: World leader in production capacity. • Guiding Opinions on EV Adoption (2014): Comprehensive support for EV infrastructure, innovation, and financial incentives.	• Battery-swapping networks in urban areas. • High-speed chargers along highways and cities. • Government financial support for public and private charging stations under renewable energy-powered infrastructure initiatives.
Germany	• Umweltbonus Program: Grants up to €9,000 for EVs. • EV Registrations: 28% of total vehicles in 2023. • Company Car Tax Reduction: 0.25% for EVs under €60,000 (vs. 1% for ICE). • Temporary VAT reduction to 16% (2020).	• Act on E-Mobility (2015): Preferential policies for EV manufacturing. • Focus on European collaborations for battery R&D. • Master Plan Charging Infrastructure II (2022): Includes private investment and digital integration for charging networks.	• Target: 1 million charging stations by 2030. • EV-ready highways: Fast chargers at service stops. • €2.5 billion allocated for expanding charging infrastructure, battery cell production, and renewable energy integration for EV charging.
India	• FAME II (2019-2024): Budget • INR100 billion for EV subsidies. • GST reduced to 5% on EVs (2019). • Demand aggregation: INR300,000 • e-3Ws targeted to reduce costs. • PM eBus Sewa: INR576.13 billion to deploy 10,000 e-buses.	• State-specific EV manufacturing policies (Karnataka, Tamil Nadu, Maharashtra). • Domestic production focus under FAME schemes. • Custom duty reduction on motor parts to 7.5%.	• Target: 4,000 public charging stations in metros by 2025. • Guidelines mandate 20% EV parking in new buildings. • Central Electricity Authority's standards for EV charging connectivity issued in 2019.

continued on next page

Table *continued*

Economy	Demand-Side Measures	Supply-Side Measures	Infrastructure Development
Indonesia	• Presidential Regulation No. 55/2019: Accelerates BEV programs. • Subsidies: ~$500 for 2-wheelers; ~$5,300 for 4-wheelers (2023). • Domestic content VAT incentive: 1% for EVs with >40% local components.	• Leveraging local nickel resources for battery production. • Focus on 2-wheelers under the regional road map for urban mobility. • Affordable EV production policies (Minister of Industry Regulation No. 6/2022).	• Pilot projects for urban public charging stations. • Private partnerships for battery-swapping networks. • Electricity discounts for home charging during off-peak hours (30% reduction).
Japan	• EV Tax Exemptions: Road tax exemption for EVs. • Gradual Shift: 100% ZEVs by 2035 under Basic Policy for Economic and Fiscal Management (2023). • Record EV sales in 2022.	• Focus on CHAdeMO fast-charging standards. • Guidelines for EV ecosystem development under Environmental and Energy Policy (2024). • Hybrid technology dominance alongside increasing EV penetration.	• Fragmented charging networks being unified under national guidelines (2023). • Development of a smart grid system for EV integration. • Renewable energy-aligned public charging stations being expanded annually. • Development of CHAdeMO fast-charging standard.
Republic of Korea	• Purchase Subsidies: Max W7.8 million ($6,000) for BEVs (2023). • Tax Credits: 15% for EV investment. • EV Sales: 52,000 units (2020). • Toll and parking fee exemptions for EVs.	• 2030 target: 4.5 million BEVs/ FCEVs under the Carbon Neutrality Scenario. • R&D subsidies for battery innovation by Hyundai and others. • Focus on hydrogen buses and high-performance battery manufacturing.	• Urban vertical chargers for space efficiency. • Expanded hydrogen and EV fast-charging networks. • Government subsidies for home-charging installations and fleet infrastructure.
Norway	• Zero Emissions by 2025 Policy: 100% ZEV sales target. • VAT and purchase tax exemptions for EVs since the 1990s. • EV Market Share: 60% of new car sales (2023). • Discounts: Max 50% of tolls and parking fees. • Bus lane access for EVs under national incentives.	• "Polluter pays" principle for high-emission vehicle taxation. • Enova Fund: Covers 40% of zero-emission transport costs. • BEVs account for 79.2% of market share (2022).	• 17,000 charging points (2021). • Fast-charging stations every 50 km on main roads. • National incentives for rural EV charging infrastructure expansion.
Taipei,China	• Green Transportation Action Plan: 100% zero-emission scooters by 2035. • Subsidies for e-scooters. • Commodity Tax Exemption for EVs up to NT$1.4 million (until 2025).	• Subsidies for domestic EV manufacturing and export-oriented production. • Leading in battery leasing and swapping technologies.	• Battery-swapping stations cover key urban areas. • Targeted expansion of charging networks, especially in rural and suburban regions.

continued on next page

Table *continued*

Economy	Demand-Side Measures	Supply-Side Measures	Infrastructure Development
United States	• Federal Tax Credit: Up to $7,500 for new EVs, phases out after 200,000 vehicles sold. • State-Level Incentives: Rebates, tax credits, exemptions, e.g., $7,000 CVRP in California. • Non-Fiscal Benefits: Carpool lane access and preferred parking for EVs. • EV Charging Tax Credits: 30% tax credit for home charger installation (up to $1,000).	• Bipartisan Infrastructure Law (BIL): Funds EV infrastructure, rural transit electrification, and school buses. • NEVI Program: Funding for deploying EV chargers and building a national charging network. • TCI: Funds EV programs via cap-and-reinvestment system, with focus on underserved communities. • TIFIA: Federal credit assistance for EV transport projects (min. $50 million capital cost). • NHPP: Funds for EV charging infrastructure on highways.	• 55,000+ public charging stations, including Level 2 and DC fast chargers. • California leads with 1.25 million EVs (2023), followed by Florida (254,878), and Texas.
Viet Nam	• Excise Tax Reduction: 1%–3% (2022). • Registration Fee Exemptions: 3 years, 50% reduction in subsequent 2 years. • Green Targets: 5% e-motorcycles by 2030 (Ha Noi); 200 e-buses by 2025 (Nha Trang).	• Localization efforts under the National Automobile Development Strategy (2021–2050). • Focus on e-bus production with international support.	• Pilot charging programs led by private firms. • Ongoing development of urban charging networks with government incentives for EVSE.

BEV = battery electric vehicle, BIL = Bipartisan Infrastructure Law, CHAdeMO = CHArge de MOve, CVRP = Clean Vehicle Rebate Project, DC = direct current, EV = electric vehicle, EVSE = electric vehicle supply equipment, FAME = Faster Adoption and Manufacturing of Hybrid and E-Vehicles in India, NEVI = National E-Vehicle Infrastructure Formula Program, NHFP = National Highway Freight Program, PHEV = plug-in hybrid electric vehicle, R&D = research and development, TCI = Transport and Climate Initiative, TIFIA = Transportation Infrastructure Financing and Innovation Act, ZEV = zero-emission vehicle.

APPENDIX 3: MONITORING AND EVALUATION FRAMEWORK

Effective management and reporting are essential for the successful implementation of the policy framework. A robust system for governance, oversight, and accountability ensures that proposed policy interventions are delivered on time, within budget, and produce the expected emissions reductions outcomes.

MANAGEMENT SETUP

To support effective planning, coordination, and implementation of the measures outlined in this action plan, it is proposed that the existing institutional arrangements within the Office of Transport and Traffic Policy and Planning (OTP) be expanded. OTP already hosts internal structures that are well aligned with e-mobility and decarbonization objectives, including:

- **Office of Transport and Traffic System Development,** which:
  - » Serves as a technical secretariat to the EV Board.
  - » Drives EV adoption and the development of supporting infrastructure such as charging networks.
- **Bureau of Safety Planning**, which:
  - » Leads the development and updating of electrification and decarbonization road maps, policies, and action plans.
  - » Oversees monitoring and progress tracking of electrification and decarbonization targets, using robust data systems for analysis and reporting.

Building on these existing capacities, a **dedicated program or taskforce** is recommended within OTP to consolidate and expand these ongoing functions under a unified operational framework. The task force will:

i) Continue and expand its role as the technical secretariat to the EV Board.

ii) Institutionalize cross-cutting coordination among government agencies, private sector actors, and international partners.

iii) Strengthen data-driven monitoring, evaluation, and reporting mechanisms to support the achievement of Thailand's Nationally Determined Contribution (NDC) targets.

iv) Provide ongoing technical assistance, capacity building, and knowledge management resources to key stakeholders.

v) Serve as the central programmatic platform to plan, mobilize, and track national investments related to EVs, infrastructure, and green freight transition.

This enhanced structure within OTP will ensure institutional continuity, build on existing technical expertise, and accelerate the scale-up of Thailand's e-mobility and transport decarbonization programs in a coherent and accountable manner.

REPORTING AND ACCOUNTABILITY MECHANISMS

Clear and transparent reporting mechanisms are essential for assessing the effectiveness of proposed interventions. The following mechanisms are proposed:

i) **Progress reports:** Implementation agencies will submit quarterly and annual reports to the EV Board, detailing the status of each proposed measure, including milestones achieved, challenges faced, and financial expenditures. Reports will also outline any deviations from the original plan, along with proposed corrective actions.

ii) **Emissions reduction tracking:** A dedicated reporting framework will track emissions reductions associated with each policy intervention. This will include a carbon accounting system that will measure the direct and indirect impacts of the interventions on greenhouse gas emissions. The monitoring and evaluation body will oversee data collection and ensure alignment with NDC targets.

iii) **Public transparency:** Key progress reports and emissions data will be made publicly available through a dedicated online portal or annual publications that highlight the outcomes of the electrification road map and the country's progress toward its climate goals. This promotes accountability and public engagement.

iv) **Stakeholder engagement:** Regular consultations with local governments, private sector actors, and civil society will gather input, ensure alignment with local needs, and strengthen ownership. These consultations will also help surface challenges and opportunities during implementation.

v) **Capacity building:** Training and capacity building initiatives will equip local authorities, transport operators, and private companies with the necessary skills and knowledge to design and implement electrification projects.

vi) **Private sector partnerships:** Engagement with the private sector is essential, especially for the development of EV infrastructure and green freight solutions. The proposed Green Mobility Fund will play a critical role in attracting private investment through blended finance mechanisms.

ADAPTIVE MANAGEMENT

The evolving nature of the e-mobility sector, coupled with the technological advancement in battery technologies, requires an adaptive management approach. This ensures flexibility and responsiveness to new developments. The following principles will guide the adaptive management approach:

i) **Regular review and adjustment:** Every 2–3 years, the action plan will undergo a comprehensive review to evaluate progress, identifying emerging trends, technological advancements, and evolving climate conditions. This will help adjust interventions accordingly to maintain relevance and effectiveness in achieving long-term goals.

ii) **Feedback loops:** Feedback from stakeholders, including local governments, transport operators, and the public, will be integrated into the management framework. This will help identify and address issues early and foster a more inclusive approach to sustainable transport development.

By establishing a clear and responsive management and reporting framework, Thailand can ensure effective delivery of the electrification action plan, delivering both climate and development benefits while meeting the nation's ambitious NDC targets.

www.ingramcontent.com/pod-product-compliance
Lightning Source LLC
Chambersburg PA
CBHW041757220926
51847CB00014B/240
* 9 7 8 9 2 9 2 7 7 6 2 9 9 *